This is the property
of:
Clara Mae
1003 3rd av
and
Elyabeth M. Riddle
Summerfield Road

ALSO BY CURTIS BOK

Backbone of the Herring

"Here, in a volume which is part fiction, part case history, part introspection and part legal philosophy, Judge Bok has produced something which is bound to be read for years by connoisseurs. . . ."

— STANLEY WALKER,
New York Herald Tribune Book Review

"The stories Judge Bok tells are fascinating, and the incidents strange, but they are such as could happen to any of us. A broad and deep humanity runs through the whole book and we come away hoping that there were more judges like the central figure of the book, Judge Ulen."

— *Commonweal*

"Curtis Bok has written a wise and delightful book. In days of violence and blood like ours, it is a heartening book to read, for it reaffirms one's faith in the humanity of man."

— MAURICE HINDUS,
Saturday Review of Literature

THIS IS A *Borzoi Book*, PUBLISHED IN NEW YORK BY
ALFRED A. KNOPF

I Too, Nicodemus

I Too, Nicodemus

BY

CURTIS BOK

1946 *Alfred A. Knopf* NEW YORK

THIS IS A BORZOI BOOK
PUBLISHED BY ALFRED A. KNOPF, INC.

MANUFACTURED IN THE UNITED STATES OF AMERICA

PUBLISHED SEPTEMBER 12, 1946
SECOND PRINTING, NOVEMBER 1946

To

Welmoet,
Ben,
Derek,
Rachel,
and Enid

CONTENTS

PREFACE

THE BOOK

PREFACE:

I Too, Nicodemus

Preface

THIS WILL BE a long preface. It will, in fact, be the book itself, and what appears as the book will be the preface, but at the end where it belongs. This has been done deliberately, for I have rarely read a preface without the conviction that it was written last, and if it were not for another and better reason, I'd call mine an epilogue and let it go at that. But I have the feeling that every story or experience or life leaves a residue born of its own momentum, a kind of cosmic verdict, and that he who tells the story or lives the experience has always a little left over when he has finished. Very often it is the most important part of all. And since the telling or the living must be done before the conclusion can be given, I shall tell what story I have to tell, then add my little extra, and rest.

What follows is intended to be neither a novel nor a collection of court stories. It falls, I hope, between the two, and is rather a piece of legal weather, a cross-section of the array of situations that a trial judge meets in his work and must solve somehow. How he solves them is quite as important as listening to the fabulous truth or reading about it, and I shall try to sketch in the well from which an average judge must draw the impulse to find decent solutions. His friends, his family life, his vacations, his religion – a little of these must be known in order to feel the integrity of experience of which his work is the outward expression. But there still remains the mystery of each man's personality, and it defies analysis. Perhaps it would be better to say that a judge's cases take hold of him and pull things out of him, and that it is his business to be sure he keeps the proper supplies on hand, so far as he can be the master of that.

A good judge must have an enormous concern with life, animate and inanimate, and a sense of its tempestuous and untamed streaming. Without such fire in his belly, as Holmes also called it, he will turn into a stuffed shirt the instant a robe is put around him. The first signs of judicial taxidermy are impatience with trivial matters and the statement that his time is being wasted, for the secret of a judge's work is that ninety-nine percent of it is with trivial matters, and that none of them will shake the cosmos very much. But they are apt to shake the litigants gravely. It is only his power over people that makes them treat him as a demi-god, for government touches them more perceptibly in the courtroom than at any other point in their lives. The cosmos is made up of little quivers, and it is important that they be set in reasonable unison. Show me an impatient judge and I will call him a public nuisance to his face. Let him be quick, if he must be, but not unconcerned, ever. Worse than judicial error is it to mishandle impatiently the small affairs of momentarily helpless people, and judges should be impeached for it.

Therefore I shall try to show a judge who had no great scholarship or dignity or wit, but a concern to be kind and patient. The cases that he handled might well be real, as I hope are the slants and pressures of his life that were the best implements he had to bring to bear upon them.

5

I

Julia

THE ULEN FAMILY lived in a small white house set on the side of a hill. They had bought it largely because it was a hill of the proper sort — wooded at the bottom, so one could not look out, and sparse on top, so one could. Most hills are the other way — farmed up close to the ears, with an overlarge hat of woods pulled down over them.

The house was modern in design, and Ulen liked it because, on the whole, he wasn't. He wasn't too sure what he was, in terms of time. He tried to live in the present, to focus his effort upon the moment at hand and be fully aware of it. This was rather different from merely being modern, biting off a morsel of time, as it were, and resting content with it. He believed that the whole of time, past and future, with all that it had meant and all that it might mean, was reduced by the miracle of a man's being alive to a unique point of consciousness, in the way a glass gathers all available light and reduces it to a single burning focus. Each person was a glass for catching time, and if one were strong enough one might even set fire to one's generation. This attitude relieved Ulen of the burden of being unduly consistent, since given moments were not necessarily consistent with each other. History seemed to him a pile of given moments constituting more a thickness of time than a record of purpose, and no proper method of evaluating it had yet been devised. Event had to follow event in such a way that they grew in a line, but many events also happened together and affected each other on a plane, and this added another dimension. The next instant with its events gave the pile its thickness. History was a slowly growing cube; each slice of events became set as they happened, and only the growing surface remained fluid. The vector of growth being unknown, there was nowhere to stand with certainty except upon the growing surface, and that was where Ulen tried to stand. When he looked backward he saw nothing but a jumble of events without the cycles or repetitions that history is supposed to have. Only here and there the shining trail of someone who believed that if the present moment were righteous the next one would be righteous too. The rest was confusion – long hard lines of independent effort crossing each other throughout the cube until they formed a wilderness. If the growing process could be turned at right angles to itself into another dimension, the jumble of events might stretch and melt into some kind of order. Through some such cleansing the race might alter its past, stand in the present, and build a decent future.

Ulen's work as judge required a degree of consistency. He was regarded as liberal or conservative depending on how excited the press happened to be at the moment. He paid little attention to that, for he believed that liberals are people who are fearful of the past and conservatives are people who are fearful of the future, and both actually spend their time obsessed by things that they hate. The present seemed to be considered an irritant to be done with as quickly as possible, a precarious treadmill between two unattainable masses of time. Ulen saw no reason to fear the present. It was his one constant possession, and if it was hateful it was because he had made it so a little while back.

He paused on his way home from the railroad station to look across the shallow valley at his house. He had turned towards the new because he thought of it as a unique growth of rose against the old arras of nature, whose ancient business was to conserve its base and broaden it slowly. He no longer wished that the house would melt and run together just a bit, for with time he discovered that its mass of angles and broken planes had a way of filling with shadows that made it appear to move about with the sun and not always to stare in front of it, stolidly opening and closing its mouth, as houses do when they have flat, square faces. The angularity let in light upon areas where he hadn't imagined he would want it but found that he did. He could enjoy his house because he spent the holiday hours of the week in it. His wife enjoyed it as one does a shop with flowers in the window.

To Mrs. Ulen, who was a cat that walked by herself, all houses were alike, and all men would have been also, had it not been for Ulen. She liked modernity because it was workable and left her blank wall-spaces against which she could put grasses or crooked branches to stand alone, like poets, showing only themselves and their shadows.

They had married shortly before he had been appointed

to the Bench, when he was in his late thirties and she about ten years younger. Their son Severn had been born promptly. When he was first permitted to see him, Ulen looked down at the child with an absent air, wondering if it hadn't been a rebirth for him as well. But people are not quite reborn, he thought, through their contacts with others, and the difference makes their dealing with each other as uneasy as it is. The baby appeared to be sleeping off the effects of a difficult experience. He lay in the early knotted slumber of infants and looked angry. The works, Ulen said to himself, regaining his sonority.

"No man," it enabled him to say, "is fit to become a father until he's forty."

Mrs. Ulen was coming out of ether and directed an unsteady eye at her husband. "It's a boy," he replied to it, "which means that *I* shall have to explain this business to him when he's older."

She relaxed. I'll mend, she said to herself, and then I'll care about it one way or the other.

Barbara came two years later. When Ulen looked down at her, the world was in the depths of economic depression and he wasn't sure that his welcome of her was all that it might have been. At least, he remarked inwardly, she isn't a boy. She will suffer, but suffering will come in by the back door; wonder if she'll be able to dispose of it by the front. That's the main job as I see it.

His first term of office had run its course and he had recently been re-elected. Severn was ten and Barbara eight when Mrs. Ulen found herself again with child. She was large and lumbered a little when she set out through the woods to meet her husband. She listened to the early summer with the withdrawn but acute perception of a pregnant mother. Each season had a sound peculiar to it. Winter tinkled like iron. The spring rent its clothes with a damp fission and sound approached. In the autumn it receded or hung, and the earth, still muffled in the stale scents of summer, rustled drily. Now there was the sound of growing fatter all about her, of a push towards overgrowth and rankness from which only the trees, most decent of living things, were free. They put out leaves, grew a little while covered, and shook them off again. The rest of the greenery grew all over, and jostled.

The walk was good for her, for the path sloped easily to the break in the hedge that Ulen had worn in the mornings, when time is stern, as a short cut to the station. She could see him coming along the road, and she needed to reach the hedge before him or he would take time to go the longer way by the gate for a look at the boxbush. She went with urgency, for she had not realized until she was well down the path that the slight tug she had felt when she walked across the living-room towards the door was not another burst of acrobatics but a pull at the perimeter, short and impersonal. And implacable, she added, measuring her distance from the hedge against her husband's. She went on faster and reached the break a little breathless and heightened as he came trudging up to it on the other side.

He smiled when he saw her, but his eyes were appraising. "Now what?" he remarked. He liked her way of announcing things and gave her chances. When she told him, he remembered how she had informed him of her pregnancy. The first touch of dizziness had caught her while she was getting out of bed one morning; she gave a little cry and steadied herself with one hand. He had raised his eyebrows quizzically.

"Tummy?" he inquired.

She had given him a flat look. "Yes," she said. "I think there's somebody in it."

She had insisted on having this baby at home, and they talked about it while walking up the path. Ulen was nervous. A man has no sense of timing in such matters and expects the first flash of pain to be followed instantly by a baby, like a clap of thunder. Throughout the evening Mrs. Ulen sauntered about, pausing to be caught in webs of pain, and when the web grew into a closing mesh she went to bed and bit her handkerchief. The doctor came about midnight and sat and smoked, but she wiggled her fingers at him and then ignored him. They both knew their business and knew that the other knew it. Uncle Michael, her father's brother who was ill and who lived with them, sat in his chair by the bookcase. Ulen did little things that were quite useless, for his wife was preoccupied. She was in a stream and the current was flowing swiftly. She could not even reach out for his hand, which he kept hopefully near. She needed her own to steer by, but for all of her efforts great stretches of the torrent rushed by without her direction. She minded that most, being caught and taken, the outcome dependent upon fortune and the subconscious address of her body. It was a strange power, this pain roaring down within her. Always down, and the rapids steeper. Her handkerchief was in shreds. The doctor appraised her and ordered the anaesthesia. She drew in gratefully. The stream levelled again, but soon the water came higher and more noisily, surrounding her with spray until she was hidden. There came a series of little jerks, like a line broken into points. Then the stream spun down into a funnel and at the moment of focus disappeared altogether.

With the anaesthesia Ulen was banished from the room. Uncle Michael had gone to bed and time crawled. The house itself seemed to be in labor. Severn and Barbara had been sent, under protest, to a neighbor's house for the night, and Ulen, alone in his home, settled down to a new acquaintance with it. The doctor's feet moved above him, slow and unhurried. At times there was a low murmur of voices. A breeze stirred the awning over the porch with a little grinding noise. The metallic pulse of the cicadas made the darkness a moving curtain of sound. The night hung gaunt and black. Almost before he actually heard the small irritated screech Ulen had started forward, as if the baby's fury had outrun its cry and reached out to warn him. There was a sharp command and the doctor's feet were urgent. Then silence fell again and Ulen forced himself to sit back and close his eyes. He felt turned inside out and even the air was astringent. He opened his mouth and breathed through it in short breaths, in order to make no sound, and his lungs seemed heavy, as if his body had become gaseous and had to be supported by the air within him. Opening his eyes at length he saw that the windows were growing bright.

A door opened upstairs and his name was called.

The doctor beckoned to him with a non-committal expression. "What would you call another girl if you had one?" he inquired.

"Julia," Ulen said obediently, staring at him.

"Fathers amuse me," the doctor went on. "They always look as if they had just been let out of a dungeon."

"They have," said Ulen stupidly. "Well?"

"Well," the other announced. "Very well. You may look at her for two minutes and then I have a job for you."

Ulen leaned over the crib and regarded his daughter seriously. "If she could speak," he observed, "I think she would say: 'Why?' "

"Wouldn't you?" the doctor grunted from beside Mrs. Ulen's bed. "Now here is something really wonderful," he continued after a minute. "Take a look at this."

He stood up, holding out the caul to the light in such a way that Ulen could see it clearly. For the first time he showed a reverential interest. He stood for a long while and gazed at it, turning the fragile membrane slowly. "Beautiful," he murmured, "isn't it?" Ulen peered at it as he would at a serpent. It fell limply over the doctor's hands like a thin veil, but where the light shone through it was a delicate lace of veins. The doctor lowered it reluctantly, rolled it together with the placenta in a piece of paper, and thrust the package into Ulen's hands. "Go out and bury it," he said abruptly. "It won't keep, more's the pity."

Ulen took it gingerly and went for a spade, not knowing what to do with it. Not the garden, where Mrs. Ulen, who cultivated experimentally, often fertilized to unexpected depths. He couldn't burn it, for the furnace was out. He decided that behind the barn was best. He was surprised to find that it was early morning of one of those fat, delicious days that only June can produce before it flares with the summer's first heat. The ground was fresh and soft, and the dew lay like unbroken balls of rain. Ulen's cow raised her rotating jaws and regarded him vacantly. Oh, she seemed to say, only an afterbirth, I just leave mine about; and she went on eating.

At the barn he caught sight of Uncle Michael, who slept badly and was up at all hours. Like all sensitive men who are forced by circumstances to live with relatives, he had achieved a minor orbit of his own within theirs, but so unobtrusively that the small contributions he was able to make to the welfare of the house were clear gifts, and he offered them as such. The Ulens anticipated his few needs and he never had to ask for anything. He returned this delicacy with a delicacy of his own, a freedom of mind and insight at the cost of a loneliness that he had come to prefer. He read widely, taught himself the language of other literatures, and kept a few hens. The result was that Michael always seemed to be present, whether he actually was or not. The passage of time had little meaning for him, and where he was concerned it came to have little meaning for the others also. He would leave a conversation in the middle if he was not satisfied with the central idea and return to it perhaps months later, after he had clarified it, as if there had been no interruption. The small breaks of life did not exist for him, and there were no salutations at morning and night. He was never surprised or upset, for his reactions to people and events came from the wide plains of his inner solitude where there were no boundaries, and he offered them with such precision that the others came to rely on him for a kind of vital continuity. He seemed to be always aware at the same level of low but clear intensity, and always available without need of preliminaries or explanations.

He glanced up a shade longer than usual while Ulen approached with package and shovel. He was completing his morning chores with the hens.

"Only two good eggs this morning," he remarked.

"Three," said Ulen without pausing.

He dug a good hole and placed his package in it with rather needless care. Strange to be burying part of a body that wasn't dead. He shovelled in the earth, took a bearing on the corner of the barn in order to remember the spot, and returned to the house, where he made himself coffee.

He was drinking it when Dr. Councill tramped downstairs, wrestling with his coat. He knew that Councill would stop and talk a little, for the doctor gave his life entirely to medicine and his only social recreation was to stay a few extra moments when he could and talk about things of interest to him. These talks, being necessarily limited, went straight to the point and stayed there. When the point began to blunt, Dr. Councill began hunting for his hat, which he had a faculty for mislaying. After he had gone, his friends reviewed their ability to see a point and stay with it for a while in profitable intercourse. The best men in any profession are essentially teachers.

Councill was broad and massive without being fat. He was simply thick. His large head was covered with white hair and he looked like a rhinoceros. This was Mrs. Ulen's idea, for she constantly saw feral resemblances in people which she explained to them had nothing to do with their character and disposition, a fact that made the search the more entertaining. There it was and no denying it. His eyes were small and blue. His nose was long and had an upward bump at the end. His wide upper lip curled away from the center like bow-waves from a ship. His head bent a trifle forward, and he walked as if holding back against the momentum of his own bulk, which gave him the air of being about to charge.

He entered the living-room and invaded a chair, holding out his hand for a cup while Ulen poured. "Fathers," he remarked, stirring gloomily, "amuse me, as I said before. What do they think about?"

Ulen regarded him limply. "The same things you would think about," he replied, "if you were a defendant on trial. They want to get out of the jam they're in as quickly as possible."

The rhinoceros shifted his weight. "Well," he said, rubbing his chin with his blunt fingers, "I suppose that's so. I remember wondering how far Julia's criminal instincts are already developed. Rather far, I should imagine. Your profession gave me the idea. How old are they when you first get them? Sixteen?"

Ulen nodded. The doctor smiled widely and made a face. "And they seem so young and innocent, on the very threshold of life, and such a pity," he said. "Much too old. Go back, way back. Not older than five. That's when something happens and we aren't priceless any more. We begin to remember. We become self-conscious, and that's the real original sin. Back of five we're criminals, without intent; and poets, without the need of beauty; and moralists, without a code. Whatever we do is right because we do it, and there is boundless trust that no matter what we do we shall still be loved and cared for. Later we swing into reverse and forget what it was like. That's the price we pay for having once been pure – that is, for having been without a sense of right and wrong. What swings us over, and why?"

"I haven't the faintest idea," said Ulen helplessly.

"Well, why haven't you?" Councill asked with asperity. "It's the key to your work. We forget the purity but it's still there, badly buried, and it comes out in the oddest ways." He paused and then said unexpectedly: "I believe in the inherent innocence of all created things. I believe in innocence but not in right and wrong. There is only the distance one can see."

"You're a communist," Ulen said rudely, for he was very tired.

Councill almost pushed his chair through the floor and got up.

"I'm not a communist," he announced. "I don't believe in commonness for the sake of commonness, or as a means of getting what someone else has and I haven't. But I do believe that if they will try, all men can become aristocrats. If I did not believe that I would shake them, as I had to shake the breath into Julia, until their necks broke. I'm off. You need some sleep. They're both all right."

Ulen saw him to the door and thanked him. Then he went upstairs and took a long time stealthily opening his wife's door. The nurse sat by the bed, watching her like a ferret, and transferred her look to him when he entered. Mrs. Ulen lay in the damp, flat slumber of the seriously wounded, but she was breathing quietly, and it was obvious that she had come through it well. He looked down at her for some time with expressionless affection. I've heard people say, he thought to himself, that they're against violence in any form. Here's nine hours' worth of the very choicest kind; the Inquisition didn't do much better in the same amount of time. He let himself out with unnecessary caution and tramped off to bed.

He couldn't sleep. It was an effort to go downhill against the freshening upswing of the day. The sunlight rang like a hammer against the ceiling of his room and flared redly under his closed eyelids, making him close his eyes tighter and raising in his ears the noise of a stick drawn quickly across a picket fence. He flung his arms above his head and stretched, feeling himself thinning until he relaxed and the heavy oil of fatigue ran smoothly through him. He flexed his feet hard and then extended them, curving his toes to touch the sheet until his arches ached and there was a knot in his calves. A returning sweetness came when he eased them slowly. He turned his head, to feel the pillow cool against his cheek and ear. The morning grew broad and heavy. Gradually he slipped beneath the outer cover of wakefulness and swam about in a half-world that melted and flowed formlessly about him like a fog, save for an intense bright light that shone around him for a little way and ended in the impenetrable fluid wall. Yet there was squareness in it, like the four-ness of two and two or of as many blocks leading ahead into the dimness: no more, hard and square in the molten mist and brilliance. He felt the breath lengthening in his throat and of a sudden sleep fell on him.

He was a sunken log, being rolled from the mud in the bottom of a stream. Up through uncounted fathoms and rigid throughout his length: little quivers at first in the deep ooze and then more violent until he shook clear of it and rose. He heard his own gasp just before he shot to the surface and awoke. Councill was standing over him, pushing at his shoulder. The window was a gray smudge of twilight. Councill sat down on the side of the bed, sloping it until Ulen had to brace himself to avoid rolling down hill. The effort cleared his head and he saw the doctor looking at him seriously.

"Narrow squeak with Julia," Councill said laconically. "Mucous. The nurse got to her in time, just as I dropped in to see your wife." He stopped and stroked his nose thoughtfully. "She was quite a pretty shade of blue."

Ulen propped himself on one elbow and rubbed his chin against his shoulder. "Anything wrong with her?" he asked.

Councill shook his head. "No," he said. "It's just one of those things that may happen to happen. What I came in to say was that when she could have died she suddenly lighted up, and it became as necessary to tell you that as it would have been to tell you she had gone. Funny," he concluded, stroking his hands slowly, "life in a few people is as positive as death. As a sheer fact, I mean, not just because they're alive. Every moment seems to be a flash, full strength, as if there were something in them bigger than their skin and impatient of it. It is like going through a fog," he said. "Even dying does not stop them."

II

Mrs. Ulen

Mrs. Ulen mended and found that she cared very much about Julia. Ulen, who was sometimes saddened by what he saw in court, did not assume that mothers always cared for their children, and he was glad to see that his wife did: even she was not exempt from the effect of experience upon his reflective eye. It would have been hard not to care about Julia, for she seemed to carry an extra lamp in her and it burned clear energy. The baby's soft but determined impact was as if she were fretting to get outside of her body and have at life more freely. If she grew up with a sturdy body she would be a great athlete, as her mother might have been if she had been interested in what her body was up to.

Mrs. Ulen was slender but she was as strong as a long steel rod and quite unsentimentally gentle. Except when she was having babies, her body paid no attention to her: it got neither thin nor fat, and it kept to itself. She treated it with similar unconcern and used it as one uses a servant who gets good wages and finds equality and freedom in service. She appeared to have a life apart from it, and she had a way of making short swift rushes at things as if she had decided to assume a shape for its general convenience but had no other need of it. If it got slightly ill or tired, she said damn and went to bed. When she handled foods or flowers, she had the air of being about to shake them for being so beautiful and satisfactory.

Mrs. Ulen seemed always to be rustling softly, and at times she pounced. Her eyes were brisk but limpid. Her voice made a small path around the letter r, and her hair was done with a few quick swoops into a knob on the top of her head. Somewhere in her laugh there was a minor third, and when she was joyous it rose to a ninth, but she left it unresolved. It was not her way to lock things in, and it was not generosity that led her to leave to everything an open end, for she did not believe that goodness was enough. Inherent honesty was better; if it was inherent and honest enough, and if it had a free trail left to it, it would approach goodness and be gay and slightly amusing in the process. The rest could be safely left to God, whom she worshipped, occasionally, with reserved respect. Life was too colorful to be withdrawn from farther: not only things but ideas had color, and tone too — china, and words, and Saturday, and relationships — and it was necessary to sort them out and translate them. This could be done only obliquely, with margin for the intangibles. When she could get hold of a shred of the color and take the cover off it she laughed, a little hopefully, and the minor third was detectable.

"Most of me is better," she said roundly about three weeks after Julia was born, "and the rest will be directly. I shall get up tomorrow. I feel a fit of fenhysteria coming on." It was her own dreadful pun and it meant window-shopping.

She got up and a few days later dressed herself becomingly in tweeds.

"I fit," she said to Ulen when he met her in the afternoon. "It's nice to look down myself from the pole and not see my clothes falling sheer from the equator."

She took his arm, squeezing it a little to herself and vibrating in a way she had when she felt alive and full of pleasure. She had on a round tweed hat that matched her suit, and when she put her feet forward she waved each one slightly before setting it down. She did not point out to him her slanted discoveries except by stopping and looking at them, her other hand suddenly on the inside of his elbow and the vibration accentuated. He felt this now and looked about him. On a small upholstery store was a sign: "Girls Wanted For Lampshades." He had been thinking that he wanted no more children: he'd kill her with all this bulging and collapsing. Aloud he said: "I saw one at the Bay once that read: 'Upper Bridge Down, Lower Bridge Up, Take Detour.'" She was thinking that it was good to be free again and that the world was quite as funny as she had remembered it. And so was he, like all purposeful men when they stop being purposeful and attempt to drift: the measure of a man's inner civilization was his ability to loaf creatively.

He was indulgent with her when she peered into windows, her face intent and appraising. He knew that she wanted nothing but new impressions that would refresh the appearance of the furnishings at home which had immured her for so long and possibly cause her to rearrange them altogether.

She paused before a window done with French period furniture.

"Bed, Louis XIV," she observed, running her eye along the ample draperies. "Lucky they had no cigarettes to smoke in it."

Ulen considered. "Too small for me. Show me a Louis XV bed. I know nothing about these things," he muttered, "but that seems logical."

She was pleased with him and called him a goose. It was such a nice afternoon: not hot, she thought, wriggling slightly inside her clothes for the pleasure of knowing that she didn't stick to anything, just a long downward slope towards dusk. Light was piled in the canyons between the buildings and there was a soft breeze in the streets. He was a dear to come with her when he was so busy getting his work done before the summer. If anyone had asked her if she loved him, she would have said, why of course: but if she had asked herself that question, she would have bitten the end of her finger and thought a while. No, she would have said, by now I live him, and that's better: he never knows what I'm up to because I don't know myself, but that's because I've given him all there is of me and don't want him to realize it. There has to be at least the illusion of me-ness about, or I'd vanish. I really do love him, another voice said in her, because he respects that last bit and just waggles his head.

Ulen was thinking that it was good to have her up and about again. I'll never get to the bottom of her, he said to himself: I try but I guess I'm not supposed to. He liked giving her things but it did not occur to him that he gave himself to her. He simply emptied out the pockets of himself and they lived together on what was there. He made a noise about his prerogatives – his claim to a littered desk, the untouchableness of old pipes, and the inalienable right of man to go out and prowl with others of his kind when it pleased him. Had he been pressed about his relations with his wife, he would have said that he had done everything he could think of and what was all the fuss about anyway. To himself he admitted with wonderment that he adored her.

"What time is it?" she asked.

"The middle of an afternoon," he said. "But take your choice. On such a day it's never stopped being about twelve years ago for me. For that worried man who just passed us it's tomorrow: he has to pay his rent and hasn't the money. For that drunk over there it's disappeared altogether. I fear it's last night for ma'm'selle approaching us.

"I forgot my watch. We'll find out here."

They were in front of a shop that did clock repairs. It was not very large but every inch of it was covered with clocks of all sizes, and every few minutes one of them rang or chimed. The proprietor was sitting just inside the door, dressed in an old alpaca coat; a watch-repairer's glass an inch long was tied to his eye by a black cord that ran around his head. He was bent over a small watch. Ulen asked the time.

"I don't know," said the man without looking up.

"I thought you might," Ulen observed, glancing around the shop.

"Natural," the other replied, "but they're all wrong."

"How do you know when to quit?"

The man looked up, one eye vast and distorted by the glass. He nodded towards a large grandfather clock in a corner.

"When it strikes a quarter to three and the hands are at twenty past ten, it's five o'clock. Then I go home. I haven't figured it out for the rest of the day."

"Same every day?"

"Same every day."

"Why not set it at five sometime just before leaving?"

"It stops," said the man. "Queerest thing."

Mrs. Ulen peered around her husband.

"Do most clocks run slow or fast when you get them?" she asked.

"Slow," the man replied. He took off his glass, and his hair was rumpled where the cord had passed through it. His large china-blue eyes were mild. "I've been adding them up. I've been here five years and I'm two weeks slow already. Thought I'd stop when I got back to the Julian calendar, but it was too easy." He paused and shook his finger at her excitedly. "I've decided to work my way back to Romulus. He had a calendar of three hundred and four days. Don't know if I'll make it. If I do, I'll stop there."

"Why?" inquired Mrs. Ulen.

"Why not?" said the man. There was silence for a minute. Then he went on: "It'll bring Christmas at a different season every year. And I'm inventing a clock that will run on the solar year: big thing."

"How do you set it?" Ulen asked.

"Set it against sunrise one day and check it a year later."

"What if it's cloudy a year later?"

The man's mouth drooped. "Hadn't thought of that," he said. "Wait another year, I guess."

"Or set it against sunrise every day for a month or so," Ulen observed, "so you'll have a margin."

But the man seemed to be on the verge of tears.

"You're confusing me," he said, putting the glass back on again. "Go away."

They backed off, murmuring apologies. "Really, my dear," Mrs. Ulen said when they were a little distance off, "you shouldn't cross-examine so."

"Can't help it," Ulen replied glumly. "It's my training, and he seemed all right at first."

Mrs. Ulen gave a cry of delight and stopped short, squeezing him convulsively. He looked at her quickly, for there was no other way of telling whether her small yelps and squeals had anything to do with what had gone before. He saw that they had stopped in front of a low, narrow passage leading into an inner court. She pushed him into it as if she had become a gale of wind. They found themselves in a court about a hundred feet long and crusted with tiny antique shops, some with miniature bay windows that had busybodies in them, and a few done with façades of Tudor cross-timbering. Mrs. Ulen had caught a fleeting glimpse of an old spindle with a rough hank of flax tied to it standing outside one shop. The place had the air of settled seclusion in which treasures are best found. Before they could look around, however, they were almost bowled over by a little old man who rushed up to them shouting ecstatically and waving his arms. He must have been quite old, for his body was bent and stiff, but he capered about on short, bowed legs that seemed incapable of staying still. It was as if life were taking leave of him downwards and had concentrated for its final effort in his legs. He ran away a few steps and then ran back again, opening and closing his mouth. There were a few brown teeth in the lower jaw but none above, and a frayed toothpick stuck upward at an angle. His pate, edged by a few white hairs, bobbed rigidly when he ran. He had the vulnerable look of the very old, as if the outer layer of him had turned to glass: even his active legs seemed to be operated by gears.

"It's my Isis!" he shouted, spreading his palms before Ulen's face and jumping up and down.

"Dear, dear," said Ulen, peering at him anxiously, "what's the matter with them?"

The little man was seized with a fury of impatience and danced around, extending a gnarled hand first to Ulen and then to Mrs. Ulen.

"No, no!" he cried, turning his head in exasperation. "It's my Isis! She has come!"

The old man's enthusiasm was infectious and the Ulens began to look about them for anything that might be Isis.

"Splendid!" Ulen cried, grinning at his wife. "My dear, Isis has arrived. Where is she?"

"I'll show you!" the old man shouted, beaming at them. "Follow me!"

He ran towards a small alley that led off from the court near its lower end. The Ulens ran after him in order not to lose him altogether. Rounding the corner, they came upon a large crate and the little old man dancing around it.

"Here she is!" he called and came up to them, blinking his faded eyes rapidly. "He put her here, but I am too old – " He laid a hand tremblingly on Mrs. Ulen's arm and dropped his voice. His eyes darted from one face to the other. "He said it is the rules. He can unload but not carry in. Perhaps you – " He began trembling so violently that Ulen was afraid he might disintegrate on the spot. By now he was almost as excited as the old gentleman. He peeled off his coat and handed it to his wife, who had been peering at the crate.

"From Luxor," she was saying. "Oh, my goodness!"

The old man had disappeared into what was apparently his shop. It was very small and quite untidy, but a few things with an undoubted air of antique authority sat with millennial dignity in the window. He emerged in a moment as if blown through the door, carrying two hammers and a hatchet.

They attacked the crate with enthusiasm. Ulen's coat was hung up on a rainspout. Several shopkeepers looked on idly from their doorways; apparently they were accustomed to the old gentleman. "My Isis, she has come at last!" he kept saying to himself over and over while he hacked at the steel bands around the crate. He looked up at the Ulens suddenly. "I could not live without her, and perhaps I cannot live with her," he said, wagging his head. "She came high, but here she is and that is all that matters. All that matters. Now careful. So." He straightened and extended his hands at shoulder level, the tips of thumb and forefinger joined. They had broken through the outer boarding and now began to remove the old papers, hay, sacking, and dirty linen cloth with which the crate had been packed. The alley slowly filled with rubbish.

At last they reached the inner core and began unswathing what appeared to be a statue about four feet high. Yards and yards of long linen bandage flowed from it. Finally they caught glimpses of stone between strips of the cloth. The old man fell on his knees. "We must stand her erect to complete the unveiling," he said in a low, trembling tone. "I never expected to live to see this moment."

The last wrapping fell and the slender granite statue stood clear. It was little marked by time and was exquisitely made. The features and headdress were trim and precise, and the delicate hands held the ankh. Timeless Egyptian calm almost breathed from it. The old gentleman rocked back and forth, touching his finger-tips rapidly to his cheeks as if anointing himself. Then he threw his hands down and his head back.

"You see," he said, husky with emotion, "very old. No horns."

"No," the Ulens said soberly in one breath, "no horns."

They gazed at the statue for some time and when they looked at the old man he had stopped rocking and his head had sunk forward. With a glance at each other they put a hand solicitously under each of his arms and helped him to his feet. Once upon them, he began dancing about again, thanking them for what they had done and asking if they could help him just a little more and get Isis into his shop. Ulen turned to comply when he heard a cry from his wife. The old fellow, in his running back and forth between them and the statue, had brushed against it. Slowly it began to topple. The old man, seeing what he had done, sat down abruptly and put his hands over his face.

Ulen dived for Isis. He reached her just in time, but in catching her he stumbled. Twisting a little, he grabbed the statue around the middle and rolled over on his back, Isis on top of him, her blank irises staring down placidly into his face.

The old gentleman was moaning: "My friends, my friends! Help me, help me! Where are you?"

"I'm underneath Isis," Ulen managed to inform him, for she had partly knocked the breath out of him. "She's all right, but she's heavy. I need a little help myself."

Mrs. Ulen's face was a study. She straddled the statue and putting her hands under its chin lifted it to release Ulen.

"Nice about there being no horns," she remarked. "You might have been gored."

"Old ladies are reasonably safe," he replied and wriggled loose. "She grew a pair later, I believe. But she stuck her ankh into my ribs and it hurts." He put one hand unceremoniously against Isis' modest bosom and pushed. Then he got up, and they carried the statue carefully into the shop and set it on the floor.

The old gentleman followed them in, waving his hands and vainly opening and closing his mouth, as if the best way of thanking them were to swallow them. He helped to brush Ulen off and found his tongue at last.

"How can I ever thank you?" he said, beaming mistily up at them. "But I must try." He rummaged in a drawer and brought out two bright blue ushebti. "Take these, please. They are very fine, but they are so little, after all you have done for my Isis."

They couldn't refuse, and thanked him. Mrs. Ulen put them in her bag. "Julia's supper time," she murmured significantly.

"One crisis a day is enough – and no funny business intended, either."

The old man showed them to the door, and when they left the court they heard him running up and down, shouting to the other shopkeepers that his Isis had arrived and that they must come to see her.

III

Meeting

AS ULEN'S WORK grew to be an idea in him rather than an activity, the need for silence grew in him too.

It was a need for margins, which generally are silent, for as his experience deepened, the law's apparent absolutes melted until the issues of do or don't, did or didn't, that accompany absolutes, grew into a new set of values tingeing the originals with the idea of might or mightn't. These new values set up a different approach. It was the approach of halving the distance to the goal instead of stopping arbitrarily and declaring that one point or another was itself a goal. A new color came over his thought, making him think that a grain of truth might be no more powerful than the flood of motives and pressures that had a way of moving it from position to position, still whole but with changing references. It was not as simple as discovering that the law is relative or that it is filled with motive and pressure because it is made by motivated and pressured men. The split between man's looking inward and his looking outward splits the law too, and it becomes of first importance to know when to apply a rule and when not to apply the very same one. It depends on whether the community's view inherent in the case at hand is outward or inward, and whether the view of the litigants happens to be slanted in the same direction. To sort out these interlacing lines takes margin and a more than conventional belief that no case is like any other.

Ulen discovered, however, that silence only made room for things to run around in and that it took agility to direct them until they ran down and stood in order. There was need for discipline to regulate the unfettered rush. He began idly to read Quaker literature and found in it a distinction between quiet, where prayer is possible and even the sense that one is being prayed in, and silence, which is only the four walls.

Ulen had been born a Quaker but for years he had taken it for granted. His legal training had done the reverse of sharpening his religion, which at its best said Do, while his profession said Don't. When his religion at its lesser best also said Don't, he had been bored by it, finding the professional negatives more interesting. The habit of being negative threatened to become an obsession: judges were often observed to sustain objections with a happier decisiveness than they showed when overruling them, and to become unaccountably cross, as if someone had left a tack sword upward in their chair. Lawyers were more effective in cross-examination than in direct. The whole tendency of the law was negative, at least in the courts, for the effort to establish breach of contract, negligence, fraud, or guilt was to show that something was done that should not have been done. It was like building a house upside down: when one had finished it and stood on the roof, one found oneself in the cellar of human behavior. Lawyers on the Bench and off had to watch out or their entire mental and spiritual equipment would go permanently into reverse.

Ulen had gone to various churches occasionally but found that he needed something other than ecclesiastical noise as a setting for a positive attitude of mind and heart. Authority was constantly being asserted with vigor, and Ulen began to wonder if the Quakers did not offer at least the chance to listen to the still small voice without an unending hubbub of prayer, exhortation, song, and gospel. The clamor kept getting in the way, and he did not believe that the congregations he had sat with had so clearly united themselves with fundamental Authority that they could partake in the discreet uproar of the churches' office hour for worship and be satisfied. They seemed rather to be thinking of all the things they mustn't do any more, and Ulen could not bring himself to believe that negative religion was desirable.

The more he dug into the literature the more it read like a testimony to quiet – a different thing from a testimony to peace, or pacifism, which he regarded as being largely a waste of time. Those who were naturally pacific would be pacific anywhere, even in the army, where a peaceful heart, being at a premium, might be able to work effectively, uncontaminated by conscience. Those who had to fight themselves to attain peace might just as well fight the national enemy for the same reason and be none the worse for it – better, perhaps, for having taken part in the streaming of the world's purpose, which is either inherently decent or else has no meaning whatever. Their abhorrence of violating the fifth commandment was generally a rationalization of a great desire to bite off the heads of people and issues and ideas. True pacifism flowed through a different meadow; it grew in quiet and gave no offense, even to error, which it tried rather to surround with benevolence than to attack. Ulen knew that he could not attain peace because he would fail to love enough, as every man has failed, since Christ. But he could try, and meanwhile decided to make no cosmic promises. He began to see that the practice of the presence of God must come by loving one man and then the next, and that by no other road could peace come.

He was not able to articulate anything so solemn. Mrs. Ulen divined it from his half-grunted remarks and his growing inclination to glower at the fire with his hair partly on end. By adroit manoeuvering she managed to make it natural for them to go to meeting some months after Julia's birth. They took a long walk one Sunday morning in early spring and passed the meeting house. It was a modest building of gray stone and old windows that made things jiggle when one looked through them. Its keystone bore the date 1723, and it had the air of having been continently at rest since then. It had a close of about three acres, protected on one side by a wall one brick wide and serpentine in shape, in order to stand up. At one end of the close was a graveyard, all of the stones alike and quite small, as if the dead had been seemly enough to push only the fingertips of their afterselves through the earth in search of the customary recognition. At the other end was the horse-shed, now converted into First-day School, and a meadow beyond.

Within there were two rooms, one for discussion and business meetings. The benches in this room were hard, and on one wall was the library — fifty books by sober authors which could be borrowed and sometimes were. In the other room the benches had cushions, for here the meetings for worship were held, and the spirit moved best from a reasonably comfortable base. In the middle was an old iron stove into which all of the male members peered anxiously at one time or another; for on occasion it grew unaccountably violent and red, and drove members into the corners for their worship, and at other times it failed to chew its fuel at all and pulled them near, wrapped in the blankets they had brought with them in case. Here were two facing benches and plainly panelled walls.

Mrs. Ulen suggested that they go in. They made their way into a corner of the meeting room and Ulen leaned his head against the wall behind him, trying to relax his mind. It was not as easy as he had expected, for the habit of quiet was in disuse, and he found that his thoughts slid around like quicksilver among such things as scraps of Meister Eckhardt's sermons that he had once read, and the name of his grandmother's cat, and a disintegrator ray of his own invention with which to shoot down enemy planes in unusually large numbers. He closed his eyes but found that he could not trust them. Against the oriental rug of light and dark the images floated against his will, and when he tried to plunge through the disturbing layer into a deeper quiet, they folded their wings and plunged through the hole with him. He raised his head and looked out of the window. A branch of the great oak just outside was rocking in the low April wind. He regarded the old tree idly and thought of Plato's remark that man is the opposite of a tree: he stands on his branches with his roots in the air. No wonder we're crazy, he reflected. A cloud went by, slow as a minute hand. He gazed at the blue beyond it, seeing it through the drift of tiny crystal splinters that curtains the vision when at rest. A leaf, brown and crisp as old paper, sauntered downwards. There was a bulge in the air, as if the earth were blowing out its cheeks.

When he closed his eyes again, the outward hush persisted inwardly. Thought had retreated but there was a sense of waiting and gathering. If he could keep at bay the restless tentacles of his mind, there would be room into which something might move; better still, something might be uncovered. For a fleeting instant he felt what it could be, like a glimmer of consciousness at the bottom of a dream. It was a deep burnished pool, alive but unmoving, and his spirit rushed towards it as a tired man rushes to sleep. In the rush it vanished, and the tentacles were about him in an instant. Gosh, he said to himself, this is going to be difficult. Then one of his toes moved, and he found that quiet had come upon him of its own accord, and that he was refreshed.

After that they attended regularly, and the meetings fell into a general pattern. In the first few minutes minds went down quickly into quiet. One could feel them rise to the surface when a latecomer opened the door, which creaked, and then plunge again. For a quarter of an hour they stayed down and reached the depth of worship; during this time they came close to one another and the unity was perceptible. Then the spirit moved and speech came. In spring the words were rounder than in the hard season, and gentler, as if St. Francis had been there and it would be fitting to take notice of it.

Minds came up and flowed with the words, and near the end of the meeting heads levelled again and the members stole glances at each other while they applied to their lives and practical situations what had been found in the silence and the speech. Early in her experience with corporate worship there came to Mrs. Ulen the picture of these neighboring minds trying to settle like a flock of birds upon the deeper steadiness of the heart. She found that she needed the quiet to slacken the steady tension of her awareness. Ulen found that he needed it to achieve an aptitude for measure as well as a practise of friendliness. It was a matter of accuracy with them both, and of a path towards a warm detachment that grows in the upper reaches of experience.

IV

Artema, Morris, and John

AFTER MEETING they walked across the field to Artema's house, where they were due for lunch. It was by way of housewarming, following her marriage to Morris Longa shortly after Ulen's re-election, and he looked forward to their first encounter on a new footing after her years of service as his secretary. Then they had worked as equals at an unequal task, and their only contacts had been in the courthouse. Only rarely had they been able to break through the gloss of preoccupation that covered their relationship in the job and let glints in to each other of the kind of people they really were. That at least was Ulen's explanation to his wife while he went along, swinging a little in his stride because of the open fields and the firm, clear morning. Mrs. Ulen smiled to herself. If men were not so obtuse, much of the world's impersonal work would not get done, and the personal work would be such an agony that not much of it would get done either. Concerned as he was over the hard cases whose perpetrators had been a bit more obtuse than he, he was able to come home, eat vigorously, and go to sleep. But Artema had several times arched her long neck and giggled with Mrs. Ulen over things that she had no business knowing about him but did. It was not Mrs. Ulen's way to let him in on such a secret, for one of her own was the knowledge that men can be very subtle about others and rarely so about themselves. His reaction to useful things when aroused was helpful to her, and his opacity regarding himself was entertaining. To make him self-conscious about either would spoil both.

They came in sight of Artema's house from a little distance. During her years of work she had saved the ample salary that the State allowed her, not for any special purpose but for whatever the inscrutable future might bring. When it brought Morris, whose resources were even more modest than hers, there was no question of what to do. With her capital and his earning power they invaded the suburbs and purchased a large oak tree, which happened to shelter a stone house and enough land to give the roots their own home and make the growing of anything else impossible. This gave the house an air of having been prepared underground and pushed up in just the right place. Some of the fieldstone in the walls, turned iron side out, looked as if the earth still clung to it. The house had bright blue shutters and a slate roof, through the center of which emerged a large chimney that did multiple service below. The north wall was a mat of ivy, and wistaria hung like eyebrows over the front windows.

Artema flew out of the door at their approach. She always held her chin high, as if she were about to float off in search of something. She gave a hand to each of them with a shower of pleasure and smiled, sighed, and giggled, all at once. Ulen looked at her closely. He saw that middle age had come like a dark wind in her face, as if dusk were needed to let her light shine clearly. There was also a new suppleness and roundness in her, or in the air about her, that abashed Ulen a little but drew his wife. It was the beginning of a relationship in which the women could take the lead and be comfortable, but Ulen could never think of Artema in any but the first capacity in which he had known her, an equal worker at the unequal task of solving problems. Life remained a business between them, and the personal sorties that were now more frequent were a delightful surprise.

Morris met them inside, also a little abashed. Meeting his wife's old friends for the first time after marriage gives a man the feeling of being caught at something pleasant but legal. He led the way to the living-room, where there was a fire. Most of the other guests were already there, and Ulen saw that it was the same group that Artema had invited to her wedding. Having no family, she had asked Ulen to perform the ceremony, and he had done so, the year before, in his garden. It was spring then too, only later, and the dogwood was out in sheaves. Ulen was affected, for Artema had told him the story of herself and Morris when they had met at the polling place on the evening of his last election day, and they had built as close a confidence as they were ever to achieve. While he repeated the words of the simple ceremony that he had evolved for weddings, he thought of her life during the years after Morris had left her, believing that she would never see him again but living in the integrity of her experience with him and wanting no other. She had made a full submission to herself, and her life had become one of oblique gaieties and of pleasure in small and unexpected things – a plant against a brick wall, a sudden lily, the balance of tiny finite things against the glowing infinite. But Morris had come back, to continue her meeting of the unexpected as being the natural course of things and he the smaller and more lovable for it. Artema had bent her head, as if sending up the short prayer that pierceth Heaven, when Ulen spoke of those who had thus been joined together in the sight of God and in the presence of this company. He paused. It was the end of the ceremony, but something more was needed. Artema, who had witnessed so many of his weddings and knew the service as well as he, did not move or raise her head. Something more just for her, after the years. He looked past them to the hill that rose behind his house. The day had let go and the light was old and rich. The little brooding hill gave him the words he sought, and he spoke them as simply as they came to him. It was the Breton prayer that he had used long ago as a boy when he said grace, seeing through the other child's eyes the rocks and the hard salt and the fires of home: "Protect us, Father. Our ship is so small, Thy sea is so vast."

They found Sam and Ida Willen talking with Nathan, or rather listening a little helplessly, as one did perforce when with Nathan. He seemed to be continually on fire over something and had the nimble intellect and forcible expression that go together in his race. It was the result of erecting into law a subtlety, not yet freed from basic mortal confusion, that drove them to seek and clarify, as if under mandate from a God as good as they but stronger, who must save not one of them but all, before He could be loved instead of feared. The

Gentile world made the obvious into law and left the rest to intuition, which so often is another word for muddle. Both wanted freedom but approached it from opposite sides — the one by seeking to cleanse the method of proof and demonstration until it could be accepted in instinctual silence, the other by letting alone until the result should come about in its own good time. Neither had perfected its own method, and hence they were suspicious of each other. Both were self-conscious, and Ulen believed that no solution could come until one man could look into another man's face and not think of its shape — or color, for that matter. He did not think that man's superiority over animals had been proved so conclusively as to warrant its application to his neighbor.

Nathan's eyebrows were as far up as they could go. It was Mrs. Ulen's idea that his hair, which grew straight back from his forehead in small tight waves, had fallen flat on his head while trying to get away from his mouth and lay there holding on. When he made a point his eyebrows abruptly retreated also, there being no telling what would happen below. Ulen approached and heard Nathan's conclusion. "It's a pity," he was shouting at Sam, "that some men don't believe in God, for they have nothing left to curse."

Sam towered above him, shifting from one foot to the other and hating to stand very long in one place, for he was tall, and like all tall men he found that he kept caving in in the middle. He and Ida had been friendly with the Ulens ever since they had come to dinner one evening and had been welcomed, warmly but oddly, by Severn, who was then two. In those days Ulen was a deputy District Attorney and tried many cases against Sam, whose quick mind but slow speech gave juries the impression that he managed to make effective points at the last moment, when the situation had almost passed him, and hence to be fighting a courageous uphill battle. What he said was plain and direct, but it was so long in coming that it struck juries as being a discovery of the crucial part of the case, when very often it wasn't. Like all men of slow speech, Sam was a listener, but he had not allowed himself to become either a rejector or an acceptor of all he heard, as many listeners do. He had a hardihood of mind that selected carefully, and he did not insist upon expressing his conclusions. Others were often not patient enough to wait until he did, for he was fastidious about expression and refused admittance to every crowd of words that appeared at his mental front door until he had chosen the ones he wanted. He mistrusted words that stood for whole ideas, like a flight of geese in a fog. He liked short, plain words that had rhythm when put beside other short, plain words. He had a way of uncoiling his long form from his chair and squinting upward at the bench. "Your Honor," he'd say in a slow drawl, putting his hands on his hips, "I don't think that's quite fair." His voice was soft but resonant, and he did not anger easily. Juries liked him and remembered what he said when they forgot or were mystified by the judge's charge.

"It's lucky you do believe, Nathan," he managed to put in edgewise. "Think how much fun you'd miss if you couldn't argue with Him."

Artema left them and went back to the front door. Dr. Councill, who had been lured from the lair of his incessant practise for the occasion, was standing in the hall looking gloomily at a small statue. "Greetings," he said and extended a hand to her without taking his eyes from the statue. "What's that?"

Artema coughed. "There were many minor Roman gods," she said. "There was Vatican, who gave babies their first breath; and Fabulinus, who prompted their first word; and Cuba, who looked after them in their crib. Walter Pater tells about them in 'Marius.' This is Domiduca, the little goddess who sees to our safe homecoming. I did it myself."

Councill looked particularly like a rhinoceros. "The human mind," he said seriously, "is like a bucket. It can hold only so much." He paused and then went on half to himself: "At least, I think that's right." He put his hat absently on Domiduca's head and followed Artema and the others in to lunch.

Talk was general during the meal, except in Nathan's corner, which he managed to turn into a small community struggling as if with a flow of lava. Artema was able to break them up at a moment when they were all shouting at once, Nathan bellowing above the rest: "I hate the law, I despise lawyers, and I detest judges."

"If he weren't a lawyer himself he wouldn't say such things," Artema commented, taking Ulen's arm. "Come with me for a moment. I have something to show you."

She led him upstairs and carefully opened a door, motioning to him to make as little noise as possible. They entered the room and Ulen found himself looking down at a small boy of about six lying asleep in the bed, his hair falling over the pillow like a pile of mahogany shavings. At the foot of the bed lay his bulldog, a vaguely rhomboid creature with Chippendale legs. The dog opened a servile but watchful eye when they came in and almost immediately shut it again. At the same time it uttered a long and tremulous sigh and put out its tongue about an inch. This was accompanied by a faint lapping sound. The boy stirred a little and Artema led Ulen to the window with barely suppressed excitement.

"Don't you know who it is?" she asked.

He shook his head.

"You put a diaper on him once," she said, "or so you told me."

His eyes shot open in surprise and he put his hand on her arm.

"John?"

She nodded, smothering a laugh and fluttering her fingers at him to keep his voice down.

"How in the name of all that's judicial – ?" he began.

"Ssh. I'll tell you," she interrupted. "You put his diaper on to show his mother how to do it. That was after I had consented to give him back to her when she regretted having let him be adopted. You remember that she brought him to the office one day, not knowing who I was. Well, I kept in touch with her after that, on the pretext that you were interested and wanted to know how they were getting along. She married but got tuberculosis and died. I happened to drop in only a week later. That was just a few months ago. I found that her husband was bewildered and wanted to go back South where he came from. I took the bull by the horns, told him that I was the woman who had adopted John before, and asked for him again. I can't have any of my own. He agreed and so did Morris, and here we are. Since we're living just over the line, we had to do it in this county, or we would have come to you."

He squeezed her arm and told her she was wonderful. "And persistent," he added maliciously, "the victim being male."

She screwed up her nose at him without answering and they stopped for a moment beside the bed before leaving the room. John was rosy and inert. He was sleep itself rather than a child asleep, and when he awakened he would again be hunger and curiosity and energy and demand, by turns. They gave him a series of personalities in the way the ranging sheaths of cloud in the sky make day a different thing from hour to hour. He had the six-year-old air of belonging willingly to anyone that really wanted him or would make even a gesture of doing so. In every soft curve of him there was the quiet assumption that he would be cared for, wherever he was, and that love could be taken for granted, shelter being in the nature of things. John had no need to love, being not yet self-conscious. He need only live, and wear the energies life put upon him, and hold out his arms.

"Nice little male, isn't he," Artema said primly. She stooped over the chair beside the bed. It was covered with crayons, envelopes and paper, and a pencil. She picked up one of the sheets of paper and handed it to Ulen.

"A letter he's written, with considerable help, to the new teacher who's coming after Easter," she explained in a whisper. "The ideas are his own."

Ulen managed to separate the long string of letters into words, and read: "Dear Miss Smith. I hope I will like you. Love, John."

"Very nice male," he commented, handing the letter back to her. "More honest than most."

They left the room quietly and went downstairs, where

they found Nathan haranguing the rest of the party from the middle of the floor. He stopped abruptly when Ulen and Artema came in.

"Nathan!" Sam murmured, "you're not abashed, are you?" He looked up at Ulen. "He's been taking you apart."

"Nothing new," Ulen said. "Shop, I suppose. All lawyers do it and it's a bad habit – therefore pleasant."

"I wasn't," Nathan stated with dignity. "I was awaiting my full audience. My point is," and he began shaking his finger under Ulen's nose, "that there's only one recipe for justice, and it's mine. Take a man and a bench. Put them together and shake well before using. Serve at ten o'clock each morning. The state of the stomach after dosage constitutes justice, and nothing else does." He paused and looked around him.

"Is that all?" Ulen asked.

"That's all for the moment," Nathan replied.

"A trifle general," Ulen observed, "but otherwise perfect. Anything else belongs in Fourth of July orations. I'm still in one piece."

Nathan looked crestfallen.

"You don't mean to say that you agree with me?" he asked.

"I do indeed," Ulen returned. "You've lumped a good deal under 'man,' but the outline is as good as it could be."

"Lumped what?" Nathan demanded belligerently. "Do you mean pity and forgiveness and compassion and severity and that kind of nonsense?"

"No. A judge outgrows those things after a short while, or he should. I don't believe any more in being shocked, even by virtue. There's one thing, though, that ought to be remembered. It's one of Matthew Hale's rules for judicial conduct, and goes this way: 'That in business capital, though my nature prompt me to pity, yet to consider that there is also a pity due the Country.' I only wish he hadn't limited it to business capital."

"The voice of experience," Ida put in. "Trite, if I may say so."

"Trite, and you may say so. But let's see. You get to see people better against the background of the Country. Better to say that after a while it helps you to let the situation speak for itself. You'll find it has in itself all the pity and forgiveness and compassion and severity that's needed, and that your own is an intrusion. You have to see it that way first. The next step isn't so trite — to get the parties to see it too, if you can. Both are steps in a process of constant re-imagining. Try it a while and see how trite it is.

"We are constantly re-imagining. When Santa Claus ceases to be real to us, we must re-imagine him in better terms, if we can find them. When we grow up and leave home, the idea of home must be re-imagined and rebuilt."

"I don't get it, said Nathan. "What's 'it', anyhow?"

"The situation, flat and just as it is," Ulen continued after a pause. "We're always dealing in court with things that people shouldn't have done. I get tired telling them they shouldn't have, and they get tired hearing me, even when it's followed by a stretch in the cooler. It's better if they see it themselves."

"See what?" asked Nathan.

"That's the point. See whatever is there to see. They imagined they understood what they were doing while they were doing it. As a result they landed in court. If they can't re-imagine their situation or have it re-imagined for them so they can see how it might turn out better for them, the whole system of trials, particularly the criminal system, is only revenge and a waste of time."

"Example, please," Councill said quietly.

Ulen laughed and scratched his head.

"All right," he said. "But don't forget that I'm not talking about right and wrong, but of how far people can see. Untangle this one if you can. I wasn't able to.

"Last year I tried a young woman named Perle D'Extase for adultery. Adultery, remember, not prostitution. She was being prosecuted by her husband, whose name was Joe Munger. She was convicted, but although it was a simple case on the facts, the jury was out for more than an hour, and when they returned, several of its members looked as if they had been pulled through the keyhole. It is my experience that jurors do the best job of re-imagining of anybody in court. We know it and we know we need it done, and so we retain the jury system. The trouble is that a jury's outlook is limited, partly because our most intelligent citizens nearly always get themselves excused, and partly because a jury's work stops with its verdict of guilty or not guilty. This may be beside the point.

"Perle's fabulous name was professional, of course. Joe, whose mixed ancestry did not include French, did not know what it meant when I asked him about it, a little irrelevantly, I'm afraid, and I gathered the impression that she had not told him, if she knew herself. I think she must have gotten the idea from an unusually spontaneous customer. She was quite an exquisite creature, small, with fine features, and an air about her, but there was languor and a hint of steel in her, as there is in most prostitutes, and a sharp look in her eye. No one in court could have missed the fact that she was playing a part.

"Joe, however, was almost beside himself with rage, and looked as if he had been steadily angry for several weeks. He took the stand with an air of iron determination and clapped his hand so loudly on the Bible that it rattled. Being Perle's husband, he could not testify against her beyond the bare fact of marriage, but he was so frantic to talk that it took both lawyers, one bailiff, and me to hold him down. The rules of evidence were a pain in Joe's neck, and he made no bones about showing it. Before we finally suppressed him I became convinced that his indignation was wholly righteous and that everyone in court held it against him.

"Perle's adultery was not difficult to prove by other witnesses, most of them hired by Joe to watch her. The case went to the jury on their evidence, but it was obviously such a small part of the real story that the jury, by nearly disagreeing, showed their resentment at not knowing more about it. But they convicted, despite Perle's denial, which may have been a trifle too demure.

"After the verdict I began to root out the story. I got part of it in court and part of it from talking to them in my office. In spots Joe was reluctant, but he came through. Perle played her hand consistently and denied everything. Joe, it appeared, had been married before to a woman who for a long time refused to divorce him, largely on account of their two children. He left her and came North from Alabama, where he had lived, and got a job as radio technician in a broadcasting studio. It was there that he met Perle while they were both working, and they struck up an acquaintance that ripened with conventional propriety. I got the impression very clearly that outside her profession Perle's affections were no easier to win than any other woman's. My bailiff, Jim Tobey, gave me that slant. He likes to talk to people after cases are over and he gets some surprising and helpful reactions. He talked to Perle after I'd sentenced her and I'll tell it his way.

" 'I sidles up to 'er,' Jim told me, 'and asks 'er how come. That's usually enough; just sidle up to 'em and give 'em the eye and ask 'em how come. They usually spill it. If they don't get it you have to ask for it. Well, she didn't get it and sez: "What?" So I sez: "How do you break that stuff in with marriage?" "Oh *that,*" she sez. "That don't mean nuthin'. That's for money." '

"It leaves quite a big question, once you get the distinction clear in your mind. Anyway, Joe thought she was as easy as she looked and when he found she wasn't he began to be interested. She was quicker than most women to detect improper advances. She held him at arm's length for some time, I gathered, possibly because she had all the clients she could handle or possibly because she saw something in him that interested her too. Joe finally found a loophole in her armor in the form of her three-year-old son. Perle had no idea who his father was, and they disresembled each other oddly – so oddly that she had had a little trouble finding the boy a nice home with people in a neighboring town. She visited him every Thursday, which was her day off. Joe went with her a few times and was so nice to the child and such a good travelling companion that she fell in love with him.

"Once won, she saw no more obstacles, and they took an

apartment together. They must have been very much in love, for they lived quietly and happily for five years, when Joe's wife finally divorced him. They pooled their rather substantial earnings and Perle did the marketing and the cooking. They both worked at night and had the days to themselves. I have no doubt that she was completely faithful to him during this time, except professionally, of course. Even Joe admitted that that was so. He seemed to understand, then, that it was only for money.

"When Joe was free at last, Perle insisted that they marry. It's one of the oddest facts in the case. Joe demurred, and that's odd too, in view of what happened later. Perhaps the oddities balance. He finally agreed, however, but on the condition that she give up her profession. She demurred to that but at length agreed.

" 'How did you get her to agree?' I asked him.

" 'I made her swear on the head of her son,' he said.

" 'No Bible?'

" 'No Bible,' Joe said, giving me a sidelong glance. 'I thought this was more effective.'

"I scratched my head over that for a while and then asked him why he hadn't objected to her profession before. He gave me a look of deferential surprise and said: 'Why, Judge, we weren't married and I thought I had no right to object.'

"I then asked Perle why she had insisted on their marrying. She gave me the same kind of look that he had given me and said: 'Judge, I wanted everything to be regular.' They nodded their heads at that. Yes, they had both wanted everything to be regular. It was about the only opinion they agreed upon.

"Joe went on to say, in a hurt tone, that he had believed her oath. He gave her a magnificent wedding and showed her off to his friends with evident satisfaction. Despite their five years together, he took the position that he was settling down to support a wife he was proud of in the way a man should, and he wanted it known. They had a brief but expensive honeymoon interrupted only by their weekly visit to the boy, and when they returned they moved into a new apartment in a better neighborhood. Life stretched ahead of them promisingly.

"A week or two later Perle returned to her profession and lied to Joe about her absences. He was suspicious, however, and soon learned the truth, which caused him to fly into a rage and move from the apartment. She turned on him for that and opened the very competent floodgates of her invective. She sought him out at his studio and made so much trouble for him there that he almost lost his job. Joe's voice was hushed when he repeated her singularly able language. He was, in effect, a whoremaster for whom she had slaved away the best years of her life, an erotic and ancestral mongrel; and she predicted that one day she would be the madam in a house where his daughter would be a prostitute. Considering her own child, it was the most potent curse she could think of. Joe's reply was to have her arrested for adultery."

Ulen paused and drew a long breath.

"How did you re-imagine that one?" Councill asked, grinning at him.

"I'm afraid I didn't do very well," Ulen replied, a little ruefully. "I tried to make Joe do it for himself and even read him a lecture on the perils of monogamy as he had found them. In cases of this kind I believe in taking the morals of the parties as I find them; there's no better way I know of to get them back to some originally honest ground. But it didn't work. Joe simply shook his head and said he was sorry but he was going to get a divorce. Possibly it's better that way. People do divorce and re-marry. Perhaps Joe and Perle, once they are divorced, will see things in a new light and return to living quietly and respectably in sin. I can imagine worse things happening to the body politic."

"And Perle?" Councill inquired.

Ulen rubbed his chin.

"Oh, I put her on probation without any trouble," he said. "She wasn't on trial for prostitution, you remember. She lied from start to finish, but of the two she had by far the more honest impulse. Joe was protecting a purely conventional position, but I felt that she may have had a less obvious integrity that she had to be faithful to. Perhaps she enjoyed being a prostitute; from the way she spoke, she had an eminent and interesting clientele, and her standards were high. No blackmail; only a detached curiosity about the colorful confidences she received, and a lethargy of memory about them as well. She gave good value and mightn't have known what to do with herself as a respectable married woman. But I am inclined to think that it was Joe's latent passion for respectability that shocked her and made her feel that he had allowed the status of marriage, with its conventions, to come between them. Their life before had been clear, but marriage was not. Some women prefer a relationship to a status, if it is real.

"I asked her if she would contest the divorce and she said

she would. I didn't have to ask her why. The quarrel was still too raw and she wanted to be able to make him support her. Maybe she will work through that stage and let him go, particularly if she wants him back again. But for the moment she was playing the game out, wagging her head at everything Joe said and making noises like an indignant cuckoo-clock. I couldn't do much to make her re-imagine the situation. All I had to offer was the suggestion that she let him divorce her and then get him back. I thought it was a feminine idea that might appeal to her, and I'm not yet sure there wasn't a flicker in her face when I mentioned it. But she brushed it aside. Perhaps she was still too angry with Joe for arresting her or perhaps she couldn't take it from a man. She gave me the kind of look a woman gives a man when she wants to pretend that she hasn't heard what she doesn't want to forget, or maybe I imagined it. She couldn't give her hand away, having played it out so far, I guess.

"She even turned her smouldering eyes on me and said: 'Judge, my word is my only honor. I didn't tell a lie.' "

Morris had left the room while Ulen was speaking. He was nearest the door and had heard John moving around upstairs. When he entered the room he found the boy sitting near the edge of the bed, his legs out and his feet sticking straight up. He was holding a small board in both hands, and his eyes were large with sudden wakefulness. He studied Morris for a moment; this business of changing fathers made it difficult to know what to call them. His new Mummy was easy, but a new father was quite a different matter, and there was something a bit out of place having him in his own bedroom. Fathers belonged downstairs. John felt dimly that he must hold his end up.

"I have an imvisible canoe," he said, "and an unimvisible paddle." Having said this, he looked indifferently out of the window.

"Where are you going with it?" Morris asked, looking about him for possible items of clothing.

"China," John replied, "but I'll be back for supper."

"Where's China?"

"On thirty parallelerattitude. You said."

"So it is," said Morris. "Where's your shirt?" He lifted the boy to his feet and began stripping off his pajamas.

"There," said John. "What's thirty parallelerattitude?"

"It's a line," Morris murmured. "Put on your shoes."

"Where?"

"On your feet."

"No, the line."

"Well, it's imvisible, like your canoe."

"Why?"

"Take your finger out of my nostril."

"Won't."

"Ouch!" said Morris, ducking his head under sudden downward pressure. "Take – "

"I'll put it in your ear then."

Morris backed off a step or two.

"You'll use it for buttoning up those buttons," he said. "Stop dancing up and down. Oh – damn it, that tickles."

"Odammit yourself," said John.

"Now, never mind," Morris said, looking the boy over

severely, "I think you're dressed. Brush your hair a little." He brightened. "As a special treat I'll let you climb up the tree a little way so you can see where China is."

John wriggled with delight. "Really, can I?" he asked, brushing industriously. "Can I take Pansy?"

The bulldog raised his head at the sound of his name and peered back at them over his shoulder, his neck and heavy snout a mass of wrinkles. Then he hoisted himself to his feet and stretched, his stern extended and his front legs flattened against the floor. In this position he gave a loud snort, then stood up and after shaking his head as if to lighten it, cocked it on one side and sat down.

"Dogs don't climb trees, dogs don't," Morris observed. "Better leave him below in the canoe."

John seized the paddle and made for the door. They clattered down the stairs, followed by the scratch and rattle of Pansy's claws on the treads.

They found the guests preparing to leave. Morris boosted the boy up on one of the lower limbs of the oak and turned to say good-bye to his friends. The bulldog sat looking up at the tree with an expression of mournful benevolence. Mrs. Ulen had to get supper and drove off in Nathan's car with the Willens, but Ulen wanted to walk and stayed behind for a moment to tell Artema that he liked her place. It was his way of saying to her that she was nice and that any place would be all right that had her to care for it. She received this gravely and then giggled in the way she had, as if putting a hat on the idea, a little askew. It was her way of saying: this is my world, all there is of it, and I think it's small enough for me to fill. Morris, who had joined them, smiled and looked at his feet, thinking that some day he might like to try filling a bigger one. Councill was looking for his hat. Artema followed him with her eyes.

"On her head," she called after him.

As he emerged from the house with it he observed morosely: "Her ears aren't right. You've left off the Darwin's points. All sculptors do."

She was about to reply when she caught sight of John, who was slowly but surely losing his balance and falling from the tree. Artema went towards him as if the air had gone from where he was and the vacuum had sucked her forwards. By the time she reached him he had fallen face down without a cry, his right arm doubled under him. He lay still for a second, dazed and sensing an unfamiliar numbness.Then he raised himself slowly to his knees and seemed to hunt for the part of him that had stopped working. As if it were disconnected from him he reached for it with his other hand and held it out to Artema when she threw herself on her knees beside him. His face was white and empty.

"Broke," he said.

Time stretched abruptly and hung while they both looked down at the queerly distorted arm. It was bent backward from the elbow. He felt no pain or fright, for more powerful than either was the instinct to know his hurt. Life had first to regroup itself or stop. The decision made, the suspended moment was released and flooded back upon them doubly strong. John moved and pain came dully. Certainty coiled about him like a snake. The arm became his again, but he had been hurt and the hurt was to the whole of him. He had not been broken before or brought up against a barrier, and he had no idea of what to do. He needed being put together, and he felt that not even the grown-ups could manage that. For the first time he was alone. He stretched his throat and gave a long, tense scream.

Artema's sheaf of terror broke at the sound and she put her arms around him quickly. Councill sent Morris for first aid material and dropped on one knee by the boy, fingering the arm gently. John felt his authority and lay still, searching his face. The doctor suddenly grinned at him. John grinned back, relieved to find that he could. Councill stood up.

"Well," he said quietly, "you've broken your arm."

John looked at it in a small flight of fear.

"No," he said with decision but as if asking a question. "Only the bones."

Councill laughed. "If that's all it is," he remarked, "I can fix bones in no time." He turned to Artema. "It's through the joint. That means the hospital and a little gas. We'll splint it now."

This was relayed to John, who did not demur. Such an important and unusual expedition met his need and balanced it. They drove to the hospital in Morris's car and Ulen went along in case he could do something. John sat very straight, holding the splint with his good hand and saying nothing. The arm did not hurt very much, and having little recollection of pain he did not pretend that it was worse than it was. He even felt important, not so much because he was the center of attention as because he was being treated as an adult. To this he responded in kind and with approval. At the accident ward they had to wait until X-rays could be taken and developed, and Ulen followed Councill into the dispensary where the doctor could fill in the time by examining other cases. There was only one patient waiting, a young girl, and she sat far back in a corner. Her face was very pale, and Ulen, who was accustomed to pallor as a sign of emotion, glanced at her eyes. In court the blood fled from people's faces and gathered as intensity in their eyes, but the girl's look was withdrawn. She was fairly well dressed but looked crumpled, and there was a bandage on her left forearm.

Councill seemed to recognize the case but not the name and asked her for it while he moved towards the filing cabinet. "By the way," he went on before she could reply, "you don't mind if my friend Judge Ulen looks on, do you? He's interested."

Ulen looked at her pleasantly and thought that she started a little. A light flashed on in her eyes for an instant and she stared at him without saying anything. Councill leaned on the filing cabinet, waiting. The girl broke her look from Ulen's face with an effort and turned to him.

"My name's Martha Tetlow," she said in a low voice.

Councill rummaged in the file and then faced her reflectively.

"Let me have a look at that," he said, coming over to her. He undid the bandage.

"Didn't I see this arm about a week ago?" he asked.

The girl shook her head. "I haven't been here before. I bandaged this myself but it's been hurting me. I burned it on a stove."

It seemed to Ulen that this was said too simply to be true. He had always believed that the best way to deceive people is to tell them the precise truth, but the precise truth is much too interesting to be told without some show of feeling. That is where liars always go astray, thinking that flatness and truth go together. He looked at her intently. She lowered her head and arose slowly, but he couldn't tell whether it was because she had lied or was in pain. All people in pain lower their heads when they get up, and the discomfort might be in either soul or body.

Councill ministered to her without further comment. She murmured: "Thank you," without raising her eyes, and left.

The doctor returned to the file. "Funny," he muttered,"I could swear I saw that arm a week ago." He searched a long while and finally produced a card. "Yes, here it is. Sara Sander. Second degree burn left forearm. Possible infection. I remember she was far advanced in pregnancy. Today she's as slim as you are and says she's Martha Tetlow. There's a mystery for you." He put the card back in the file after making a note on it, and turned to pick up the X-rays of John's arm which a nurse had just brought in. He put them in a shadow-box and studied them carefully.

"Bad break," he observed, "but the young heal easily. Send John in, will you? I'll see you later."

Ulen returned to the room where the boy was waiting and told them that the doctor was ready. Artema and Morris arose with more than usual alacrity and their eyes met. Morris all at once found himself incapable of further usefulness. He felt himself turning a pale yellow and stood aside.

"You go," he said stupidly to Artema. "I can't. Sorry. I could if I had to, but I don't have to and so I can't. See?"

Artema saw and patted him. She would have insisted upon going for the same reasons had she been told to stay behind.

It came out at the same point for them both. John also absolved him with a glance. Fathers were always going places or not going, and their absences were unfailingly important. He slid off the bed where he had been sitting, took Artema's hand, and made for the door.

She tried to make it easy for him to take the gas but failed. When he saw that she was going to allow an unknown indignity to be visited upon him he knew that he had to stand alone and was too little to know how. He had been betrayed. The nurse, the doctor, and his new Mummy were stronger than he, and he didn't know what was about to happen to him. He had to match his wits against it and against all of them as well. He began a delaying action, his mind working as fast as it could to invent small needs. He had to have a drink of water; he needed it badly. He had to go tinkle. If he was to go to sleep there had to be a story and then prayers. He pointed to the window to show that soon it would be getting dark. He had forgotten to brush his teeth and wanted to very much. He had to think faster and faster when they brushed these orderly things aside one by one and brought the unknown nearer. There was nothing left to think of now; it drew closer and poised above him. The figures around him were enormous and incalculably strong. He began to howl and they had to hold him. Something was on his face and he couldn't howl properly in such a small space. He shook his head savagely from side to side to free himself from it, but that made him lose his breath and gulp for air. He found that it was rather fun to spin a little, so he gulped again and spun more quickly.

Artema was tired when she finally stood up, lifting her shoulders and pushing her hands over her hips to smooth herself. She had let him be frightened but she did not know what else she could have done. She rested her fingertips on the end of the operating table and looked critically at John. His head had fallen on one side and he was breathing almost angrily, a few damp hairs clinging to his forehead. It is pain that really separates people, she thought. She felt a fleeting resentment that Morris had let her take the brunt of it alone; but he and John were already separated, being men and knowing that it is wise not to suffer in each other's presence. She knew that men must measure each other quickly and that age and relationship have nothing to do with the process; but suffering in silence has a great deal to do with it. It went back to their both being bulls and each having to know what kind of bull it was he had to deal with. She sat down helplessly while the doctor set to work.

Ulen walked up and down with Morris and helped him smoke. He said little, thinking it best to leave his friend to his own devices. The situation was not serious, but that has little to do with how a person takes it. Morris was vulnerable to the accidents and dislocations of life. He had once been in the gutter, and of the few men who can shake off its potent lethargies and rise from it, none comes back insensitive. He bore its scars, however. He could happily make and keep appointments with other men, but being approached for advice or help gave him a slight feeling of being trapped and of wanting to run away. And he showed some impatience with those who could not take the road that he had taken, for he knew that it was not wholly their fault that they were where they were. The pit that he had dug for himself would have held him irrevocably if he had not realized that it was not only he that had dug it. His first wife, whose weaknesses alone matched his, had dug it foot for foot with him; a drunkard herself, she had made one of him, and together they had squandered the modest fortune that he had inherited. When he could accept that fact, not as a judgment of her but as the cool balancing of a bill, he was able for the first time to shoulder his share of the blame and deal with it. The gutter is negative, and it flows with abasement. Fewer men have been crucified on the plus sign of ambition than have been impaled upon the minus sign of guilt.

If Artema suspected that he had fled to her for security in his struggle upward, she gave no sign of it. But she did not suspect it, she knew it, and it was all right. She seemed to know that it was all right from her first look at him. A woman, she thought, must have creation about her, and only when he struggles does a man create.

She had not hesitated when he appeared, after more than four years' absence. He came one day in the late autumn while she was typing an opinion for Ulen. A high wind was driving the dust against the tall courthouse windows until they rattled angrily and boomed with sudden glassy claps of noise. The door opened and when she looked up she saw Morris. She made no move except to take her hands from the typewriter and put them in her lap, and watched him. Our child is dead, was her first thought; she would have been nearly four. His eyes were on her and she could see hunger in them, faint under his obvious control, but they were steady, and there was no embarrassment in his manner. At only a slight widening of her eyes the years fled from her, and she waited.

Morris put his fingertips on the glass top of the desk and smiled down at her.

"When I went away," he said, "you told me that when I was ready I would know what to do. I would now like to take you to lunch."

She looked briefly at her watch.

"In ten minutes," she said, "when I've finished this."

He sat down and watched her unobtrusively. The swift staccato of her typing, the ping of the machine's bell at the end of the lines, and the booming of the windows were the only sounds. Once she bit the end of her forefinger and bent over her notes. When she had finished she pulled the paper from the machine; it came away with a low screech and flapped softly while she removed the carbon from the copies. Then she arose and took the original into Ulen's office, and Morris could hear the brief murmur of their voices. When she returned she took down her coat and hat and put them on. She fished in her handbag and powdered her nose briefly, turning it a little and examining it for flaws. Putting the compact back into her bag, she turned and for the first time smiled up at him.

"Now I'm ready," she said.

She saw him often after that, letting him come and go easily and without demand. He made none, for they both knew the path they were on and knew where it was leading them. And they walked along it happily, knowing that in its own good time it would turn a corner. It did, one day in March, after they had eaten their lunch hurriedly in order to have time for a stroll in the little park next to the courthouse before they returned to work. The day was still and there was warmth in the sun. They sat down on a bench, saying little and watching the pigeons settling with a dry flurry of wings on the ground and waddling hopefully near their feet. Morris snapped his fingers noiselessly at the bravest one and the bird regarded him critically, clucking fatly to itself.

"It's nice here," he said, "on a day like this."

"Yes, it is," she replied. "This kind of day has curves."

He grunted appreciatively.

"Usually March is the forgotten time of the year."

"How?"

"It's like the hour from three to four in the morning, when things stir that aren't alive yet. We should have one long February and then go straight into April."

She made no reply, for she knew that the path was turning. There was no reason why it should just then, but time had levelled and had gone from them, leaving only day and now and themselves. He turned to her.

"Look at me," he said. For a moment she bent her head and then raised it to him. "I love you."

She leaned back almost limply and gazed ahead of her at the courthouse window, feeling that his eyes were on it also and that he knew what she would say. She spoke it as if her heart were bare to him.

"I love you too," she whispered.

Morris fretted while they waited. He felt responsible, having let John go up the tree, and it caused him to envision the worst possibilities. No more reliable doctor than Councill, but accidents do happen. He arranged the funeral in his mind. Dismissing that as silly, he pictured the boy going through life with a withered, crippled arm. That seemed silly too, and he realized that it left him little to worry about. But it was taking an endless amount of time and he said so aloud. Ulen sucked at his pipe and reminded him that Councill was probably putting on a cast. Morris felt better and became aware of a submerged relief that it would prevent his teaching John to swim that spring. Lucky it had happened now, or the summer plans might have been ruined. He'd make it up to the boy by reading to him, a thing that he disliked intensely.

Once or twice he tried to peer in the dispensary window, but it was too high, and all that he could see was the top of Councill's head occasionally when the doctor moved around. It seemed to be unhurried. For the most part he sat with Ulen on the low wall that ran beside the door and watched the light begin to fade. A chill crept into the air when the sun went down and at last they shook themselves and went inside. Morris ventured a look into the dispensary and saw Councill completing the cast. John was awake and his cheeks were rosy. He was wrapped in a blanket and looked up at Morris languidly and without expression. Artema was sitting beside him, holding his free hand and listening to the doctor's instructions. They consisted mainly of informing John that he must stay out of trees.

"There, now," he concluded, "we mend him and wrap him up, but we don't deliver. Take him home." He patted the boy on the head and tramped off after his hat and coat.

Ulen and Morris lifted John between them and carried him to the car. Artema got in first and took him in her lap. He lay back against her, subdued and looking out dreamily at the deepening twilight and saffron in the sky. A pile of ashen clouds, painted on their western edges, sank in great steps below the tree-line; between them were streaks of green, and through windows here and there the far and ultimate blue. He had never been outside in the dark before, and the world was magnificent and strange. He knew how the dark came at home, from the slowly retreating walls and the caverns that grew there, with monsters in them, until the light was turned on and they bounced back into place again. Later, when he was in bed and Mummy turned out the light finally, the darkness pounced and took away everything in a flash, leaving his bed floating in a prickly, tingling void kept at bay by the comfortable close armor of his sheets and blankets. But out here the darkness came like the water in his tub, creeping up his body until it covered him. The saffron was dulling to a scarlet smudge, and the leaves of the trees above him rushed at him down the yellow corridor of the car's headlights and swooped into blackness over his head. It was wonderful that the car could go so fast in the dark, or even that it would consent to go at all, this being the time for all things to be asleep. It sang to him that it was going home and taking him; there was no other place in all the world to go, and it sharpened the adventure to know that they were going a little out of their way to take Ulen to his home first. Strange that other people should have homes. They weren't like home at all, for home was where I am, the little, hunted, creeping I.

The car stopped and voices broke his reverie. Ulen was leaning over him to say good night. It did not matter what he said, or why. There was only the tall, striding adventure of the dark that might be shared a little. John looked up solemnly at Ulen.

"I'm out in the dark," he said, "as a special treat."

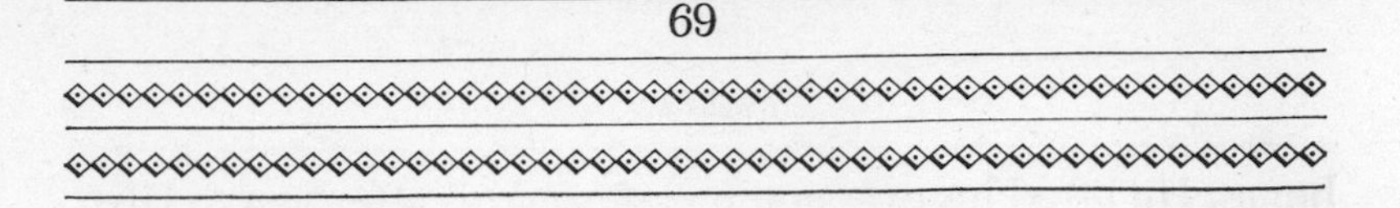

V

Severn and Barbara

Ulen walked up the path to his front door. The air was fresh with the young darkness and felt washed. He opened the door, and the welcoming warmth of the house, with its habitational odor faintly suggestive of almonds, beat about him and raised a little blaze in his cheeks. He blew on his hands, rubbed them together, and hung up his hat. Hissing and scuttling noises in the kitchen informed him that Mrs. Ulen was preparing supper. He poked his head in to announce his presence and explain briefly what had detained him. His wife, dealing hardily with spinach at a critical moment, made a wide arc with her head and said something inaudible to the spinach; her mouth was pursed and she was concentrating. Ulen backed off and returned to the living-room.

Michael was sitting in his chair, the lamp beside him framing his frail body and the book he was reading in a yellow cone of light. His skin looked as fragile as tissue paper and his head was large and soft, as if the intensity of his thought were eating its way outwards and had already absorbed the bones. He lifted his eyes and transferred his attention to Ulen without seeming to stop reading. Then he lowered the book gently and leaned back, sighing a little and closing his eyes.

Ulen crossed the room. "Tired, Mike?" he asked, lowering himself into a chair.

Michael smiled but did not reply. He did not answer such questions, since he was always tired, but the others asked them of him as they did of each other, and his silence seemed to make it a little better. He sat and listened while Ulen recounted the events of the day, seeking, as the handicapped do, a common source or pattern in what he heard. It was his habit to regard speech as a bird flying over rough country, and he kept an eye on the obstructions that cast up air currents and disturbed its flight. He assumed the bird's integrity but not the country's, and when he spoke, his comments ostensibly had more to do with the problem than with his companion. Narrative drifted by him in small pieces, like snow driven by the wind. His ear caught something about reimagining and clung to it until his mind had closed around it. He glanced up at Ulen.

"You'll be a long time coming to the end of that," he said. "You might try practising it on the children."

"I know," said Ulen.

"You don't," Michael returned equably, "you've no idea."

Mrs. Ulen appeared at that moment, wiping her hands on her apron, and rang the Chinese gong that announced meals. Ulen went to wash his hands. Michael slowly pushed back his chair. As if touched off by the gong, young but very strong voices rose in song in the upper reaches of the house. The rhythm was marked by a vigorous stomping of feet; the children, arms at their sides and jigging in unison, were revolving rapidly at the head of the stairs to see who would get dizzy first. The old song swelled to its climax:

> The cow kicked Nelly in the belly in the barn,
> The cow kicked Nelly in the belly in the barn.
> The farmer said it wouldn't do her any harm.
> Skip doo-ralloo, my dar-ling.

There was a thud and a high soprano squeal. Then the sound of a minor avalanche gave notice that Severn was coming to supper. He was perfecting a method of appearing to fall downstairs without actually doing so, and he reached the bottom stern first.

"How was that one, Mum?" he asked breathlessly, looking up at his mother.

"Quite good," she said casually, "but I think I like the broken leg sequence better. It's more startling and noisier."

Severn jumped to his feet.

"Yep," he said seriously, "but gee, Mum, it's hard to do. I might really break it."

"Not so long as you're trying to," she commented, "but you will some day when you're getting out of the bathtub very carefully."

While her mother was speaking, Barbara glided backwards down the stair rail like a small white spider on its own thread, and stopped herself expertly an inch from the spike on the newel post.

"Really, my dear," Mrs. Ulen said, glancing reproachfully at her husband, "you must remove that thing. It's getting in

Barbara's way and it's better outside than – " She twirled her fingers without finishing.

The children slid into their places and looked hungrily about. The Ulens bowed their heads.

"Grace," said Mrs. Ulen.

"Whose turn?" Ulen inquired.

"Hers," said Severn.

"His," said Barbara.

Mrs. Ulen looked up sidewise.

"Severn," she murmured.

Severn sighed deeply, his thoughts wandering.

"Aw gee, Mum," he said and his eyes darted around the table. Then he suddenly announced: "Silent," in the tone that he had once used to his father when he had done something he shouldn't: "You can't spank me, Daddy. You're a Quaker."

He bobbed his head until his nose was in his plate. Barbara wriggled and scratched her neck.

"Hurry, Severn," she whispered hoarsely. "It's omelette."

Severn raised his head abruptly and watched Mrs. Ulen go for the omelette with the maddening restraint so common to mothers. Ulen was looking down his nose with judicial impassivity while Michael, crippled as he was, arranged himself in his chair. Barbara was in a flat calm. Severn, to fill in the crevice of time, began to intone: he had qualified himself as an expert in the jargon of advertisements.

"Fertilized eggs from fecund hens," he murmured. "Children cry for coverfast, homogenized, irradiated milk: we respect the individuality of the cow. Eat miracle bread, it's vitamin-enriched, it's slo-browned. It's hydroformed. It's polarized. It's nuts."

Mrs. Ulen appeared with the omelette, holding the plate gingerly at its far ends and leaning a little backward to escape its hot breath. The omelette was set down and duly dispatched. Ulen fixed his son with a meditative eye.

"Severn," he said, "what did you learn in First Day School today?"

"Wear Avalanche garters," Severn replied indifferently. "Guaranteed to reach the floor of the finest drawing-rooms. Keep your hot-dog hot with Hell-Fire mustard. Does he bring friends home to dinner? Throw a party quickly with the new Vesuvius cooker. For the middle-age spread use a Boa-Constrictor girdle. Find permanent relief with Death-Rattle cough-drops. I made those up myself," he added modestly, pausing for breath. Uncle Michael's mild gaze floated over him and came to rest on Ulen.

"When?" Ulen asked.

"In First Day School."

"What did the teacher talk about?"

Severn's eyes swept across the ceiling and he ran his fingers swiftly through his hair.

"Aw gee," he said. "We learned all about Nicodemus." He stopped abruptly. Mrs. Ulen had gone for more food, and he glanced around as if a little relieved.

Ulen settled himself comfortably.

"What about him?"

"He wanted to be born again," Severn stated decisively, "but he couldn't make it. Pretty ghastly."

"Ten years' experience in criminal court," Michael remarked, "put in a nutshell. Go on from there, Your Honor."

Ulen opened his mouth to go on but Severn was off on another tack. His mother had returned and birth was not a subject that seemed to offer free or extensive possibilities.

"Superman," he chanted, "exerted all his super-strength and absorbded the volt-rays of the vile traitor in his bellybutton."

"Absorbed," Ulen corrected him, "not absorbded."

"How do you know he ab – did it in his bellybutton?" Barbara was all eyes.

"It's the only place he could do it," Severn answered with dignity. "The vile traitor aimed the volt-gun right at his stummick."

Barbara had every appearance of being about to say something decisive, but Mrs. Ulen put in hastily: "I suggest navel instead of bellybutton."

"No," he said, "it isn't so good. You can see it better when you say bellybutton."

Barbara was curious. "Mummy, is that what it means when it says in the paper: 'The deceased was a Naval surgeon'?"

"No, it isn't," Ulen said with emphasis. "It only means that he worked in the Navy. This is getting difficult. What did *you* learn today?" He looked sternly at Barbara, who sucked the end of her thumb.

"The teacher told us," she reported after thinking a minute, "never to hit back."

"Well," Ulen said suspiciously, "was that because you hit somebody back?"

Barbara's eyes were round with honesty.

"Oh no, Daddy, I don't ever hit back," she responded. "I always hit first."

Ulen groaned. There was a chuckle from Michael. "There

you are," he observed, "spoken with urgent, honest warmth. You may cross-examine, counsel."

"He snatched my doll," Barbara explained.

"Was he larger or smaller than you?" Ulen asked.

"Smaller, of course," said Barbara, lifting limpid brown eyes, "or I wouldn't have hit him."

"Was he the little colored boy I've seen there?" Ulen inquired.

Barbara pondered a minute. "I don't know," she said, "I'll look next Sunday and see."

"What happened then?"

"He gave my doll back."

"Well, that's good," Ulen said. "It was nice of him to give it back."

"He had to," Barbara said simply, "or I would have kicked him. I was all ready to. I'm going to kick him next Sunday."

"Why?"

"Because he told the teacher."

Ulen pulled himself together.

"Now look here," he said. "Why didn't you let him play with your doll?"

Barbara studied, swinging her foot rhythmically against the table leg.

"I didn't want to," she said.

"Why not?"

"Because."

"Because isn't a reason."

Barbara was growing sulky. "I'm going to kick him," she said stubbornly, "right in the snoot."

Ulen looked helplessly at his wife. "Your witness," he said.

Mrs. Ulen fixed her daughter with a feminine eye.

"You bring him to me," she said, "and let me kick him. I can kick harder than you can."

Barbara flared. "You won't either," she cried. "I want to kick him all myself." But she had begun to laugh a little. Her mother leaned over and patted her.

"There, you see, dear," she said, coming down on the idea like a hen on the nest, "you really like him very much and don't mean it."

"I do too," Barbara retorted, half laughing and half crying. "He wants to marry me, but he's too little."

VI

Bowen

WHEN ULEN went to work next morning he found Nathan and Harper Burns waiting in his outer office. Nathan, aloof and respectful, was obviously there on business. Burns was the city's best trial lawyer. They had a case, they said, specially listed for today, and they had come to him ahead of time to tell him that it would most likely take a month to try; he might have to make special arrangements. He thanked them and strolled down to the jury room to ask for volunteers. Such a long case would carry the jury beyond its normal period of duty, and he wanted only those who were willing to stay the full time.

He read the pleadings [1] while the lawyers were striking the

In these footnotes, nomenclature and details will be found to differ from State to State, but the ideas involved are, I believe, general. Needless to say, they have been severely boiled down here. Lawyers will know how much has been left out and are expected to be lenient.

[1] The papers. A plaintiff must file a statement of his case and stand by it, for his opponent and the Court are entitled to know what's bothering him. In most cases the defendant must file an answer, for the plaintiff shouldn't

jury, [2] and learned that it was a suit against an insurance company on various fire policies. A business establishment had burned and the insurance company had refused to pay. The defense was fraud: a hint that the plaintiff had set the fire himself, and a direct charge that he had overloaded his payroll and inventory in making his claim. It looked like a long dull case – a month of rummaging about in records and wrestling with figures. His impression was confirmed by the few people in court. Beside Burns at the defendant's table sat a cadaverous person surrounded by a small mountain of ledgers. Behind him on the floor were two packing cases of books and records. The insurance company had probably spent half the amount of the claim in resisting it. At the plaintiff's table Nathan chewed his pencil and searched the faces of the jurymen. At his elbow was the plaintiff, George Bowen, already in a lather of perspiration. Throughout the trial he rained steadily. He was young and fat but looked strong, and black hair stood out from his cuffs. He appeared to be a person of boundless and communicative energy, for he frequently leaned forward to whisper in Nathan's ear, his legs and arms as tight as sausages in his clothes. It was plain that he annoyed Nathan.

be in the dark either. If the defendant has a claim of his own, or if he injects new and devastating matter, the plaintiff may reply. There it stops, but in the very old days it went on and on, the antagonists thrusting away at each other with replications and rebutters and sur-rejoinders, and if everything wasn't just so, down to the last to-wit, there was hell to pay, and it usually wasn't the plaintiff.

[2] Assault and battery is not implied. Twenty jurors are presented to counsel when a case is called for trial; if there are more than two litigants with separate interests, four more jurors are added for each additional party. Each party may then strike off the names of four jurors for any reason or no reason. The net result is twelve jurors.

Behind Bowen was seated a young girl with a pile of documents beside her. Most likely his secretary. Her appearance startled Ulen. She had on a long green dress which had obviously been made to curve with her. It accentuated the shallows and suggested the depths. A line from Herrick drifted through his mind while he looked at her: "then (methinks) how sweetly flows that liquefaction of her clothes." A green hat with a broadly sagging brim shadowed a very blond face. She was Nathan's major mistake, for not only did she sit in the same chair during each day of the long trial, even when she was not needed to locate papers, but she always appeared in precisely the same ensemble. Mrs. Epps, juror number eight, was Nathan's minor mistake. She was a prim and elderly woman who plainly disapproved of Maria early in the trial and never relented; a tart, Mrs. Epps could almost be seen saying to herself, and a dirty one at that. The chance that the girl had no other clothes did not seem to occur to her. She spoke her mind to Jim Tobey about it after the trial.

The case did take nearly a month. Maria took the stand on the second day, and when Ulen thought it over later he decided that Burns's short cross-examination of her was the crisis of the case. Her name appeared to be Maria Solley. Yes, she had been Bowen's secretary; she had kept the books and typed for him. She described the system of records, and identified papers. She had gone home early with a headache on the day of the fire, which occurred in the evening, and she knew nothing about it until she came to work the next day. Bowen had gone on a business trip and she couldn't locate him until nearly noon. He had returned at once. She gave her testimony in a low, rasping voice, as if it were past history of no great importance. Nathan waved her over to Burns.

Burns addressed her quietly and directly, pausing after each answer. He asked her only a few questions but they were very skilful.

"You live where?" She gave the address.

"That is where your parents live, is it not?" It was.

"How long was it before the fire that you were not living there?"

"I don't understand you."

"I think you do, Miss Solley."

Nathan got to his feet.

"Objected to as irrelevant," he said.

Ulen sat up. Not much hope of diverting Burns but he'd have to try. The most he could do was bluff, but he had to be careful of the effect on the jury. He declared a short recess and summoned the lawyers to his chambers.

Burns's square face was impassive. Ulen regarded him thoughtfully.

"You're trying to get in the subtle idea," he said, "that she was his mistress. You know as well as I do that it has nothing to do with the case. If you go on with it I may declare a mistrial and it's too late to get on the list again this spring. Your people have spent too much on this case to let it drag. Think it over."

Burns looked like a dog with a bone.

"I have thought it over," he said. "We claim that the records are false and incomplete. I have a right to show where they were kept and how they were kept. If there are any attendant inferences, I'm entitled to them."

Ulen turned to Nathan.

"Why don't you settle it?" he asked. "They'll spend quite a lot on Mr. Burns alone, at a couple of hundred a day in court. You see what he's doing to you already. Better take any decent figure you can get and run. How do you stand on negotiations?"

Nathan spread his hands. Burns looked pained.

"We won't pay a nickel," he said. "It's a fake and we won't buy it even if we spend twice the claim on the trial."

Ulen had to give up. The questions were technically legitimate.

"All right," he said, "I can't stop you, but watch out if there's a motion for a new trial. Don't forget I can grant them without reasons 'in the interests of justice.' Let's get back to work."

"I'll take the chance," Burns remarked grimly.

They filed into the courtroom and Burns resumed his questioning.

"Were the records kept at the shop?" he asked.

"No."

"They were kept in a house at 120 North Burley Street, were they not?"

"They were."

"Mr. Bowen lived at that house, did he not?"

"He did."

There was quite a long pause, during which Burns did not move but gazed at her intently.

"And you stayed there too, did you not?"

Maria looked at him, dropped her eyes to his waistcoat, and lifted them again.

"Not all the time."

"But most of it?" Burns persisted.

"I had to," she replied. "It was a new business and we worked night and day."

"What were your wages, please?" It was a matter of record.

"Fifteen dollars."

"Did you get it every week?" That too was a matter of record.

"No."

"That's all, thank you."

If Maria hadn't sat there day after day in her increasingly wrinkled voluptuousness Nathan might have turned the tide, but a pall of inertia seemed to settle over the jury from then on, and they resigned themselves to their fate of listening until their moment of release should allow them to speak for themselves.

Three days followed of wrangling over the arrangements and admissibility of records. It was the hardest part of the trial for Ulen, who felt about figures as he would about standing between a hungry lion and its supper. Questions of admissibility he waved aside. He believed in letting in the whole picture so far as possible. In civil cases lawyers had the curious idea that they were trying situations only. Ulen felt that in every court proceeding a human being was also on trial and that the laws of logic applied to him in no greater or lesser extent than they had done while he was building up the situation. Bowen, asserting a claim that was being resisted on the ground of fraud, was certainly on trial.

He was the only other witness for his case. He was on the stand in chief for a week and under cross-examination for two weeks. The main burden of preparing the case had been on him, with some help from Maria and legal guidance from Nathan. Some of the records were missing and the rest had been kept rather casually. He approached the witness chair mopping his neck. His voice was harsh and arrogant, and his words came like a rush of water from a drain. He began by saying that he had had to go to work when very young, his parents being poor, and that he had not gone farther than the eighth grade in school. An objection from Burns was overruled. He had married early, struggled hard, and had not been particularly successful. In an odd moment he had thought up a new kind of valve for a steampipe, and with what money he could scrape together he had leased a small abandoned shop in a back lot and begun manufacturing. After five years of incredible labor he had brought the situation to a point where it would hold together and make a little money. He had sent his wife and child to live with her parents and ploughed back his earnings into the business. He took barely enough for himself to live on, but he had some orders for his valve and he believed in it. Some day he would be successful and have a home for his family. Burns objected tersely and was overruled.

Just when he was beginning to see his way clear he had some bad luck. His largest shipment was returned because of faulty performance, and he had to admit later under cross-examination that he had used inferior metal in order to make delivery on time. Other orders were waiting, but he had no credit or cash. His creditors began hounding him. There was no room left in which to turn, and in desperation he took a train and went to see his largest creditor in the effort to stave off bankruptcy. While he was gone the fire broke out and destroyed the plant. Except for the insurance he was broke.

His voice faltered when he said this and he had to mop harder. Burns again objected and was overruled.

Bowen concluded his general testimony: "I've been working selling ice-cream cones for the last few weeks but they fired me yesterday because I took so much time off over this case." He shaded his eyes with one hand and stopped.

Burns arose, buttoning his coat. "I now move that a juror be withdrawn [3] and the case continued," [4] he said with an air of finality.

Nathan unexpectedly objected. He probably thought that he had erased the impression created by Maria. Ulen gazed morosely at Burns.

"Earlier in the trial," he observed, "you showed considerable interest in Mr. Bowen's life. I think we had better hear his whole story. The motion is denied, with the usual exception." [5]

---

[3] This is legal shorthand for declaring a mistrial. It would of course be simpler to say "mistrial," but the past is ever with us. The full technical procedure was that if something occurred during the trial so prejudicial that counsel for the offended party believed that his client could no longer receive a fair trial from the jury in the box, he moved to have one of the twelve withdrawn. If the judge agreed, a juror was escorted, rather to his astonishment, from the courtroom, whereupon counsel objected to proceeding with only eleven jurors and was sustained, perforce, by the judge. Nothing for it then but to get a fresh jury and start all over again, usually at a later date, after everyone had cooled off.

[4] The opposite of what it seems. It doesn't mean to go ahead. It means to postpone the trial until a later date, usually as the result of a mistrial or unpreparedness to proceed: in short, to continue the Court's jurisdiction over the case until it is finally tried.

[5] By pronouncing this magic word, a lawyer who has suffered an adverse ruling saves the point for later argument on appeal: if he doesn't say it, the appellate court will consider that he has waived it. This is an example of legal shorthand. Until comparatively recently there were no court stenographers, and something had to be done to get the incident on paper if the appellate

The rest of Bowen's testimony concerned the records. Maria's year of business college was just enough to enable her to keep them in some sort of order, but there were broad gaps and errors, and Burns insisted on all of the technicalities. Ulen sustained him more often than not on this branch of the case, for Bowen had to prove his case no matter how pathetic he tried to make himself appear. He had a thousand things to do besides keeping records, and he hadn't had much education. Maria wasn't a very bright girl either, he added with a short laugh, looking down, but together they had done the best they could. His memory was surprisingly clear when there weren't any entries. He'd rub his chin and look at the ceiling and say yes, he remembered that particular shipment, with dates and prices. He'd been too busy to put it down at the time and had forgotten to do it later. Now he remembered, but oddly enough he couldn't think of the shipper's name. Funny he'd forget that. Not finding it on the ceiling he looked for it on the floor and snapped his fingers, as if it could be summoned back within tongue's reach. Well, he was sorry; it had escaped him.

It didn't take Burns's long and merciless cross-examination to convince Ulen that Bowen was laying it on too thick. Had

court was to know what had happened at the trial. This was done by stopping the trial while the objectionable question or answer was written down, together with the judge's ruling. The fact of aggrieved counsel's exception to the ruling was also noted. The judge then examined the paper, which was called "a bill of exception," and sealed it if he found it in order. It was then ready for presentation to the appellate court later. This is no longer necessary when there is a full stenographic report made of the trial, and the appearance of the word "exception" is enough. Some judges still pay tribute to the old procedure by intoning: " Objection sustained. Exception noted. Bill sealed." But the modern tendency of appellate courts is to reverse for fundamental error whether it is tagged with an exception or not.

he tried the case early in his judgeship he would have smiled grimly and helped to expose what is conveniently called an imposition on the Court. He knew now that it was nothing of the sort. No Court can be imposed upon unless it permits itself to be, and Ulen regarded the lengthy trial as a lesson in industrial logistics that Bowen had to learn the hard way. He did not think of it even as a moral corrective. Too easy to lug in morals and righteousness; they did not leap from one man's forefinger into another man's soul, but grew or were acquired through the filter of living. And might be found, in the same man, to apply to some things and not to others. Morals are supposed to grow spontaneously in high places, and the temptation was great to hand out a few ready-made from the Bench. Ulen had come to see that this was a mere escape. Bowen had to be led back over the ground. No use unless he saw for himself. In the larger sense, Ulen reflected, he was conducting a class, for few people believe that they have done wrong until they have been found out, and they must first be shown the extent to which they have been. If regeneration is then to come, it can come only from themselves, voluntarily and with grace. It was the only way to make peace with a malefactor, whether a law breaker or the national enemy—to hold him firmly but patiently until he could in honesty forgive himself and make a new start.

Ulen closed his eyes and tried to form a clear picture of Bowen. Most important to get straight was the man's powerful drive to succeed and his obvious fear that being left behind would be the ultimate in tragedy. So great was the fear and so important the end that the means suffered and hence the end would be blunted too. Bowen had fallen into the old pit of using poor means, thinking that he could forget them once he reached his goal. But forgetting would not be enough. If he did reach his goal it would likely turn its face from him. If he lost it outright he might forgive himself and make a better start. Ulen looked at the means in order to be sure. Yes, they were shabby enough from what he had heard. Suppose it was worse; suppose Bowen had set the fire himself. Well, that was not horrifying in itself, it would be only more of the same thing. Cleaner too, perhaps, when Bowen came to make amends to himself; easier to forgive oneself a great sin than a small one. Ulen had no fear about its coming out in the trial if it had happened. The resources of the insurance company, headed by an avenging angel like Burns, would not fail to dig it up. Only it must come out clearly. No more innuendoes like those about Maria. Even a sinner should not be hinted into hell; too easy to turn his acknowledgment of error into rage at the method used against him. He braced himself to remember.

He was roused from his reverie by hearing Nathan say: "Cross-examine."

Burns wasted no further time on personal matters. He felt he had done all that he need do of that, with Maria. For two weeks he hammered Bowen on his records and figures, and when he had finished they were in shreds. But figures are stubborn things and don't reduce easily. Burns had to go with care, for he needed Bowen's co-operation in arranging the items the way he wanted them, and he ran the risk of letting the jury think that he regarded this part of the case as crucial and Maria as a diversion. He took the chance, however, for he knew his ground well and finally made Bowen's juggling of the figures look like an even greater enormity.

Near the end of his cross-examination Burns called on Nathan to produce all of the correspondence that Bowen had had with his principal customers during the year before the fire. After hearing arguments, Ulen concluded that the request was legitimate and directed Nathan to comply. Bowen scratched his neck and mopped vigorously, shaking his head. He'd do the best he could but it would be a tremendous job; well, if he had to he had to.

He needed the documents that he had with him in court to help him locate the letters. It was a heavy load, but he and Maria got them out of the courthouse and into the battered old truck that had escaped the fire. They bounced along without saying much. It was a dreary day, with clouds and rain like dripping lead, and when they reached the house on Burley Street it was filled with an even, cheerless damp. Maria had moved back to her parents' home after the fire, but Bowen had stayed on, not wanting to return to his own family until he had re-established his business or had played his last card. The insurance money would put him sufficiently on his feet to go forward again. He occupied only two rooms, one of them filled with litter from his business that overflowed into the other room and almost filled it also. Piles of old letters and files stood in corners, most of them half covered with heavy pieces of rusted pipe or partly made valves. He had turned the place upside down getting ready for the trial, and it was now in a state of complete confusion. The air smelled of wet dust and the chill beat upon them. The bed was unmade and there was no heat.

Bowen stood and looked at the scene of desolation. Maria shuddered and blew on her hands. She wasn't working and had come willingly to court as his witness. Now she followed him to the house, not out of loyalty or even out of interest, but because it was something to do and because the momentum of the trial had made the decision for her. She lived in a vacuum, and if one moment of her time made a demand on the next she followed it by a kind of capillary attraction. Anything outside her could draw her attention because there was very little inside her to hold it. She had drifted into Bowen's way of living because it was single and easy to follow, even though the work was hard. Her feet now took her to the stove, where she looked around for something to cook for supper. On the stove she found a paper of matches; imbedded in the cover were her initials, M. S. He had once given her a box of them as a present, and they had both used them. She glanced at it for a moment without expression and with an indifferent gesture wrenched loose a match and lighted the gas.

Bowen attacked a dusty pile of correspondence and glanced up at her.

"I'm afraid there ain't much to eat," he said, "but there's some. I don't know where to begin on this stuff." He began to whistle, a little shrilly. "Gotta be done, though," he added in a tight voice. When she had supper ready they sat where they could and ate it in silence. Funny girl, he thought to himself; funny how she came here and did what was needed. Didn't have time to do nothing but work. Never gave her nothing but those matches. She worked as hard as she could too; has a lot coming to her in back wages. Hell, women are funny. Aloud he said, deprecatingly: "Looks like an all-night job. I only found three letters from Wilson so far and I know there's a stack of 'em."

"Yeah," she said, "there must be a good stack."

After supper they set to work in earnest, but progress was slow. They turned up the desk lamp to light the room. It was the only light he had, and the filaments glittered painfully when they turned their eyes towards it. At about three in the morning Maria lay down on the bed for a nap. He went on working until five, when he raised himself wearily and looked out of the window. It was still stormy and another gray day was sliding into place. He got up and stretched himself. He was tired. Maria lay sprawled on her back across the bed, her knees drawn upward and one arm over her face. Fatigue was running in him like a cataract, and he felt himself melting with it. He lay down beside her and fell asleep at once.

Half an hour later he struggled back to consciousness and lay face downward, not thinking very much. Only impressions came, worn like over-used cuts. The day in court, the ceaseless struggle of the months and years before the fire, other nights of work with the tension of pursuit and worry overlaid upon the tension of his drive to succeed. He got to his feet with a little groan and pulled himself together. Maria was already at work again.

By seven o'clock they stopped and faced each other.

"We're only half done," Bowen said, tensing his mouth. "Looks like another night's work. We'll have to get along in court today with what we've got."

"Yeah, looks so," she said. "I'll get some breakfast. Jesus, but I'm rumpled."

There wasn't anything to eat except coffee, some crackers, and a couple of apples, and they ate this at a dead low ebb of vitality. The rain made long, broken pencils on the windows, and the wind was somber. After breakfast they freshened up a little and felt better. They put the letters that they had found into separate envelopes, hauled their load of papers to the truck, and made off to the courthouse. By the end of the day Bowen looked haggard. Every question that Burns asked him seemed to open a fresh gap in his defenses. He was neither humble nor intelligent enough to believe that he could lose his case. To him it had become an endurance contest, and he settled down to show that he could take it. The fact that he was being relentlessly exposed as a liar and a cheat did not appear to disturb him. He couldn't believe that any jury would refuse to give him back his business from an insurance company. He stuck out his chin at Burns and did the best he could. He was dull but dogged when Ulen adjourned for the day, and his shoulders sagged when he lifted the heavy pile of papers again and with a nod to Maria made for the door.

On the way to the house they stopped and bought a few supplies, including a bottle of whiskey. The rain had stopped, but the wind muttered in the loose sash of the windows. They took an hour's nap before supper, but the insufficient sleep lay upon them like an extra burden when they roused.

"Feel lousy," Maria said, shaking back her hair and raising her eyebrows above her closed lids in order to snap them open.

"Yeah," he said. "We better have a snort."

They had a couple of snorts and got supper mechanically.

Their heads buzzed with fatigue and the liquor hit them low, so that they buzzed all over. They moved at half speed while the whiskey rose to their heads and lightened them. Maria prepared supper and put the food on the packing box that they were using as a table. She fell back into the one chair and hung her hands listlessly over the arms. The veins running into them looked like blue rivers on a map.

"Let's get drunk," she said, her eyes closed.

"Nix," said Bowen. "Wait 'til we get the verdict and then we'll get pie-eyed."

She did not demur. One thing was pretty much like another, she thought – getting dead beat or getting drunk. They came from the same thing. The electric impulse of the idea shook her, and she pushed herself forwards with her shoulders from the back of the chair.

The food and drink raised their spirits considerably and by the end of the meal they had the loose hilarity of tired people. Maria took off her right shoe and scratched her instep.

"Jesus," she said, "I could kick that guy Burns right in the gut. What's he trying to do – kill us?"

"Hell, he ain't getting no place," he observed, and smirked. "We made plenty mistakes but who doesn't? Any jury'll go for a guy who went broke in a fire."

He lighted a cigarette and left it in one corner of his mouth while he turned the match cover over and over with his fingers. M. S. He gazed at the letters reflectively and started to say something, but checked himself. He glanced up at Maria, who looked back at him steadily. No use going over that again. Burns hadn't asked either of them about how the fire started, and if he hadn't by this time maybe he wasn't going to. Let it go. He tossed the matches aside with a grunt and got up. "Come on," he said, "let's go."

They made progress for the first few hours, but after midnight the dusty confusion became stubborn; files were incomplete or intermingled, answers were found to inquiries that were missing, many were torn and the parts separated. They were down to their last reserve of strength and worked automatically, as if capable of only one more motion that had still to be divided into uncounted parts. The unassorted files shrank upon themselves and brooded malignantly. Bowen felt empty of blood. By three o'clock they were sick with fatigue and had to stop. They fell on the bed and were asleep in an instant.

He kept on falling, straight through the bed and into a universe of gluey space that held him and rushed past him instead of leaving him free to fall. It was a kind of flight, but his arms, which should be outstretched to steady him, were doubled under him and he fought to loosen them. The space had neither beginning nor end, but there was a sense of beginning towards which he was falling; it was lighter there, and the other way was clotted with massive granite clouds. He wrenched his arms free and swooped this way and that to avoid them, but they rushed upon him and surrounded him, rising harshly in jagged towers while he threaded his way desperately among them. He was flying through a narrow canyon, barely missing the growling walls that snapped shut behind him, keeping his way by a frenzy of attention.

Suddenly he grounded and found himself standing on a wide plain without sound or limit, save for a sense that hung in the air and filled the universe with an unformed calculation. It became part of the air he breathed, and he felt a power dragging it inexorably towards formulation; it slowly gathered shape and took all attributes and sensations from him, leaving him bone-dry in the empty immensity and pulling him towards itself. The shape gradually became visible but unnameable, and the vacuum created by it was a torture. Then from the shape came realization of what it was, shot from it to fill the vacuum in his mind, and he knew that it was drawing both him and the emptiness about him. It was he alone that must reach it, and he was freed a little to move forwards stubbornly. Slowly the shape became money in hard round bags, burning against the dead emptiness in which he moved and with which he was competing, a skeleton driven by a nerve. The money glowed at an incalculable distance, and in the ashy emptiness he moved towards it, bound by a heaviness against which he labored an eternity to gain a step. There was a buzzing in his ears that wove a wall of silence around the emptiness, and with the silence came an utter cold. He was conscious only of the wriggling nerve within him, but the air was steel that clamped and held him until he could move no longer, while the money grew in splendor. Little by little there came an absence of cold beneath his feet, and through his numbness it grew to be a spot of warmth. The money had drawn all other light to itself and the blaze of it increased, but no heat came from it. There was none but where he stood. He had shrunk down into a tiny spot of warmth. It was all there was left of him and he felt himself pitiful. Tears ran down his cheeks, but they were cold and left icy channels on his face. He started in terror and cried out, but the emptiness swallowed the sound in his throat. He gripped the warmth and moved, but the motion brought new cold and a shaking agony of fear. Nothing existed but the little spot of warmth and it was barely enough to hold his bones together. Imperceptibly he felt the flat tension increase and stretch him past the point where he could break and die. The glowing bags of money were receding from him into distance beyond imagination and he was tied to them, but he could not move into the obliteration of that outer cold. The warmth held him with a fleeting promise until from the farthest reach of consciousness, growing from a speck into an obscene roundness, the shape of zero rushed at him: absolute zero, carrying the vacancy of complete extermination. He clenched his teeth wildly. It hurled itself at him with the speed of light, and when it burst in a million fires before his eyes the thing that tied him snapped, and he floated queerly upwards, holding the formless promise to him.

Suddenly the universe reeled and quaked around him and thunder rumbled about in it. He started into wakefulness to find Maria shaking him angrily. "Hey! What's the big idea?" she was complaining in her grating voice. "Keep your big mitts to yourself. You just socked me in the mouth." She felt her lips tenderly and looked at her fingers with a sulky expression, and then fell back on the bed again.

He muttered an apology and dragged himself to his feet. He yawned and forced out his held breath sharply, trying to drive his eyes open. He pushed his wrist out of his coat-sleeve to look at his watch. The numbers looked fuzzy and he drew his mouth far down in order to get a focus. Seven o'clock. He cursed and turned to Maria, but stopped and scratched his head deeply with his nails. Let the kid sleep. No need for her to kill herself. He sat down in the chair and frowned; damn funny dream, he couldn't remember much of it, but he felt warm and slack, and his eyes roved wearily over the remaining piles of correspondence. He took them up listlessly and worked a little while, but finally he lay back and dozed again. He couldn't get all the way back to sleep. He'd done enough, he'd let the rest go; some things a man couldn't do, or perhaps he was just too tired to give a damn. Must be going nuts, having a dream like that. He'd lie back and think about it; guessed he couldn't think, he'd just rest a while. One hell of a fight about something, but he buzzed pleasantly now. It was nine o'clock when he opened his eyes again, and he jumped to his feet with an oath and awakened Maria. She sat up and made a face, stroking her mouth gently.

"You big lug," she muttered, hiking up the back of her dress. She shook herself and went to the stove. "I'll get some coffee," she said crossly. "We better eat something."

"I think we're done," he said. "Done enough, anyway."

"I should hope to Jesus we're done," she said flatly. She sat down, holding her chin in one hand, and watched the coffee boil. When it was ready she poured some into a cup and held it out to him indifferently.

He drank the coffee listlessly and felt its warmth. The same warmth stealing through him. He looked oddly at the black stuff in the cup and turned it with severe deliberation in his hand, as if he had never seen it before. He closed his eyes momentarily, focusing against the lids. The image of an empty dead cold was there, but now he saw it rather than felt it, for the warmth held. When his eyes opened only a vestige of it remained, a flatness of memory, but it persisted. All at once he realized that he had forgotten the case, and tension returned in a small hard ball, like a cord suddenly knotted. It passed almost as soon as it had come, and the flatness reasserted itself, but shot through with a steady flicker of warmth. He shook his head again and frowned, and there was a dark echo of fear. He got roughly to his feet and spat on the floor.

"We're late," he said. "Get a wiggle on."

They loaded their papers into the truck and reached the courthouse ten minutes late. Ulen glanced at him sharply but at the expression on his face said nothing. Several of the jurors looked at him curiously. He got into the witness chair quietly and for the first time sat back. Burns did not spare him but grilled him mercilessly on the correspondence that he had produced. He had had no time to look it over carefully, and he did not realize until well into the morning how damaging it was. The knowledge drifted through him like a passing cloud. In its wake came the thought that he might lose the case after all. He smiled grimly but did not move in his chair; what's the matter with me, he said to himself, I can't fight. He became aware that the warmth was still in him, not a glow but a bare comfort; at the thought of fighting it chilled a little, and he sank lower in his seat to bring it back. He was conscious that the courtroom was quiet, and glancing about him he discovered that the jury and both counsel were looking at him. He must have missed a question. He turned to Ulen and squeezed his nose between his thumb and forefinger. "Sorry," he said shortly. "I been up two nights getting this stuff. What was the question?" The judge was a remote black mountain, not so much a man as a neutral presence that he could hold to.

After nearly two weeks of cross-examination he had forgotten Nathan. What with nearly going nuts and seeing things, he had lost his fear of Burns and had trouble even paying attention to him. The jury now seemed to be against him. His whole interest had swung to the judge as the one level thing in the long stretch of the trial. Only once, when Ulen asked him a question, did he look at him squarely; there seemed to be a glint in the judge's eyes, neither of hostility nor of favor, but like two pools far up on a mountain. In his weariness he had to struggle against turning to him and saying: "You decide it, Judge, and let me go."

He was so tired by the lunch recess that he put his head in his arms on the counsel table and fell asleep. At a word from Maria, Nathan left him there. Ten minutes before recess was over she brought him a sandwich and a bottle of milk and roused him to eat it. He felt a little better when he went back on the stand. Burns, aided by three men, was unwrapping a small package with extreme care. He sat down and gazed at Bowen with more than usual intensity.

"I have only a few more questions to ask," he announced, clearing his throat. "You say you were out of town when the fire occurred?"

Bowen nodded.

"Speak, please," Burns said viciously. "I want your answers to these questions to be very clear."

Bowen lifted his eyebrows. "I was," he said.

"And Miss Solley has testified that she went home early with a headache on that day. You heard her, did you not?"

"I did."

"Where did the fire break out?"

"So far as I know," Bowen replied, "it was in the waste room."

"That was in an out of the way part of the plant, wasn't it?"

"I guess it was."

"Did either you or Miss Solley have frequent occasion to go there?"

"She didn't have no reason to go there," Bowen explained. "I didn't have much neither. The helper always dumped stuff or got stuff there. It was a kind of a place to put rubbish."

Burns pursed his lips and looked thoughtfully at his fingers. Then he abruptly reached in his pocket and threw down on the table beside the witness chair a paper of matches.

"Whose initials are on that cover?" he demanded.

Nathan leaped to his feet to object: " — unless it is first shown where they came from," he shouted.

Bowen stiffened and his hand shook. He reached for the matches and heard Ulen lean forward to rule on the objection.

"M. S. Maria Solley," he said quickly, without looking up. "I gave her a bunch of them once." Nathan subsided with a puzzled look.

"And did she use them?" Burns inquired.

"We both did when we needed them."

Burns arose with emphasis. "I will now ask you to look at this," he said, lifting the package from the table before him and carrying it gingerly to the witness chair. He turned to Ulen.

"I suggest to Your Honor," he said, "that this has been prepared by the State Chemist. The box is closed with his seal. Can you tell me what it is?" He addressed Bowen again while he lowered a small glass box onto the witness table beside the matches.

Bowen looked at it glumly. In the glass box was the reconstructed ash of another paper of matches. The imbedded initials M. S. were clearly visible.

"What are those initials?" Burns's voice was like a whip.

"M. S."

"Would you say that this was the same," Burns touched the glass box and then the match cover on the table, "as this?"

Bowen did not move from the rear of his chair. Too clear. No use denying it.

"Yes, I would."

"My last question," Burns remarked in a low voice. "Would it surprise you if I suggested that the ashes of these matches in the glass case were found in the waste room where the fire started?"

Nathan arose with a roar, holding up both hands and preventing his client from answering. "I now move for the withdrawal of a juror, if Your Honor please," he cried, "unless Mr. Burns not only proves his suggestion but gives further proof that my client, alone or in conspiracy with Miss Solley, set this fire. His suggestion is an outrageous innuendo unless supported."

Burns faced the bench.

"I'll try the case in my own way," he snapped.

"In order to clarify the situation," Nathan returned, "if Your Honor will allow me to reserve the right to ask my client a few obvious questions in case Mr. Burns agrees to go forward with his evidence, I rest."

Ulen nodded and looked at Burns. "I accept the reservation," he said. "And you?"

Burns looked at him squarely.

"I rest upon the plaintiff's case," he said, "and will present no evidence."

Ulen was annoyed. Burns couldn't prove the connection and was going to hint the sinner into hell after all.

"I am prepared to grant the motion," he said.

Burns interrupted him. "Will Your Honor hear me?"

"I think it unnecessary," Ulen said sharply. "Without proof of a connection between your exhibit and the plaintiff I consider his case to be clearly prejudiced. Someone else might have dropped those matches there."

He finished speaking and saw out of the corner of his eye that Bowen was talking busily to Nathan, who looked bewildered and in a moment stepped to the bar.

"Will Your Honor indulge me a moment before acting on my motion while I talk to my client?" he asked in a strange tone.

Ulen waited while they retired to a corner of the courtroom and whispered together. Burns sat down and looked hard at his feet. Bowen kept Nathan about five minutes and seemed to be pleading with him. Nathan often broke in to explain with despairing patience, as if talking to a child. Then he rubbed his chin and approached Ulen with his head bent, thinking.

"Your Honor," he said, "my client insists that instead of withdrawing a juror and continuing the case, we suffer a voluntary nonsuit.[6] He has asked me if Your Honor would speak to him."

---

[6] The plaintiff may quit at any time if he gets cold feet or his proofs fail him. He may then start a new suit if the Statute of Limitations hasn't run out; if it has, he can't.

Ulen glanced sharply at Bowen and reached for the pleadings. The jury looked like a pack of hunting dogs whose prey threatened to escape them.

"Mr. Bowen," he said, "has your counsel explained to you that if you suffer a nonsuit you will have to start a new action?" Bowen nodded. He was very calm now. The whole mess could be cleared up between him and the judge.

"And that the Statute of Limitations [7] now prevents you from starting such a new action?"

"Yes," Bowen answered.

"And also that if I withdraw a juror – as I am willing to do – you may try your case again at a later date?"

Maria reached out for Bowen's arm, casting a furtive eye at Ulen while she did so, but he moved slightly out of her reach and nodded again. Maria arose and without a glance behind her marched out of the courtroom.

Ulen looked steadily at Bowen. He did not fully understand what was happening to the man, but he knew that it was not possible for a trial to yield full understanding. He felt that Bowen had reached a turning point of some kind and needed only to be heard.

"Why do you want to throw up your case?" he asked as kindly as he could.

Bowen, faced with the question, could not explain. Perhaps he could not explain even to himself. He only knew that he was tired and empty, save for the warmth that had remained with him all day. He looked out of the window and mopped,

[7] You can't sue people after a certain time, usually from one to six years, depending on the case. Claims get stale: witnesses die, evidence disappears, or people forget. A suit started after the time limit will be thrown out if the defendant objects.

trying to reach words. He glanced appealingly at Ulen and shook his head.

"I got too much to beat," he said.

Ulen regarded him meditatively for a moment.

"Very well," he said.

He made the appropriate entry in his docket and raised his head to the jury.

"You have sat here patiently," he said to them, "for nearly four weeks, and it would be natural that you should feel disappointed by not having a chance to render a verdict. Mr. Bowen has decided to abandon his case, which he has the legal right to do at any time until a jury has spoken.

"I should like to divert your disappointment if I can. We do not know what has prompted Mr. Bowen to give up at this point in the case. He has told me that he feels he has too much to beat. It would be easy to say that he means he has been beaten in the trial. I should say that he has been, and I think it likely that you would find in favor of the insurance company." Several of the jurors, particularly Mrs. Epps, smiled grimly and nodded. "But there is always the chance that there is more to it than that. This long and exhausting trial may have done something to Mr. Bowen that nothing else could have done. We do not understand the human heart very well, another's even less than our own. His case, in my opinion, has been prejudiced by the production of a match box reconstructed from ashes and bearing Miss Solley's initials, without proof that either he or the two of them together set the fire. I would have had to declare a mistrial in any event. It was too great a suspicion to be thrown into the case without support, and it could not be properly compensated, in my opinion, even by Mr. Bowen's flat denial. In fairness to him we must reject any such suspicion.

"It is also easy to say that he has surrendered because he saw that too many of his lies have been discovered, but there is the possibility that he has looked back over his actions and seen them in different colors. I should like to think so. I should prefer thinking so to believing that another liar is crawling out of court with his tail between his legs merely because he has been found out. You may believe whichever you please, but think about it. Regardless of how you decide, I urge you to think of a trial in court not as a trap for catching people, nor as a waste of time if it stops before you give a verdict. It is better that Mr. Bowen see the light and you feel some disappointment, than it is that you do your conventional duty and Mr. Bowen feel that we have all been unfair. For weeks he has sat before his judges – you and me. He has had to reconstruct an important period in his life for us to measure in silence until the time came for us to give our judgment. That is an important and a searching process. We have been for four weeks the anvil on which Mr. Bowen has been hammered, and I think that the result has been a good one. It is not necessary that a law suit be won or lost, but only that understanding come from it. You and I have been a kind of school in which a fellow citizen has got an education, for his voluntary surrender shows that he has learned something.

"Remember, if you sit in other cases, that while you are judges you are schoolmasters too, and that it is possible for anyone to re-value his life and take a better step, even at the last moment.

"Thank you for your patience, and good-bye."

When Ulen finished, Bowen raised his hand with timid concentration, then turned to Nathan and spoke to him briefly. Nathan smiled and scratched his head, looking up at Ulen. Then he walked over to where Burns was sitting and appeared to ask him a question. Burns threw up his head with a little humorous snort and made a wide gesture with his hand.

"Your Honor," Nathan said aloud, "my client has asked me if he might have the matches and the glass box. He says he'd like to keep them as a souvenir."

VII

Bring; Paltrey; The Little Man Who Glowed

In May Ulen began his three months' duty in Criminal Court. It was the hardest time of the year for him. Criminal cases were tried in a separate courtroom, a dreary place so sodden with tension and misery that in the fairest weather it felt damp, as if covered with mould. It was haunted by eyes, tens of thousands of eyes that had looked at every inch of it until it seemed soaked with old dead sight. Eyes even more than voices had sunk into the marrow of the room. His own, during long examinations or speeches by counsel, had explored every leaf and crevice of the dark, ornate ceiling. There had been the eyes of spectators dull with apathy and sitting in the courtroom merely to keep warm; the eyes of relatives of victim or prisoner, predatory or anguished; the eyes of those who came only for the thrill of murder or rape; the attentive eyes of jurors and counsel; the eyes of the court officers, case-hardened after years of service into a kind of agate look, but interested in spite of themselves; but the eyes of defendants most of all, like those of animals seeking escape or resigned to anything but uncertainty.

It was here that the past was dragged into the present through a knot-hole of rules and restrictions and compulsions, until the room had acquired the look of an old man with sunken cheeks. It had grown hard and narrow, from the dull linoleum on the floor to the square, high windows that for years had not known any curtains other than the mustard-colored shades that unrolled with a harsh screech and kept out the afternoon sun. The seats were straight and wooden, and even the black leather on the judge's chair had been compressed into a curved, unyielding pad: under it the springs had become so worn that the chair tipped to a compulsory angle and required effort and a great squeak to force it to sit upright. The ceiling that soared above at an immense and needless height writhed in an agony of gilded domes and terraces and leaves until it seemed that the building must have shuddered and wrinkled itself. The walls were panelled to a third of their height in false mahogany and above it rose bleakly to the ceiling in dull yellow plaster. Light came from an enormous chandelier hung in the middle of the room, groaning under the wasted weight of plaster scrolls and tassels.

In this spacious sepulchre no one could speak naturally. Loud voices boomed and awoke a thundering echo. Light voices were swallowed altogether. Witnesses, already ill at ease or entirely terrified, were constantly being told to do things with their speech that were unnatural to them. Judge Brennan, an enterprising soul, had ordered an amplifier to be installed, but the authorities did not get the right kind and the thing spent its time wailing like a banshee or adding such a metallic edge to the voices that it got on everybody's nerves and was abandoned. Nothing that has been tried and failed has a second chance against the imperturbability of municipal finance, which is so imperturbable that it is a wonder anything gets tried at all. Ulen discovered that curtains had once been hung in the windows, but the exclusively masculine taste that dominated the city government had decreed thick drapes of dark green velvet; they had added so ominously to the gloom that when they had become laden with soot and grime and had fallen down of their own accord, no one had bothered to put them up again. Since the city offered only white or yellow paint, yellow had been put on and allowed to darken slowly into a flat, diseased-looking ochre that deepened into honest black in the corners. White had been considered as being too vulnerable to dirt, and regular repainting was unheard of.

Ulen had to fight against the lethargy of this gloomy place, and the vitality of the cases helped him. Day after day they flowed past him in a stream, ranging from number-writing to murder. Sir Matthew's pity that was due the Country seemed at times too ready a refuge, particularly in the severe sentences that the Country expected in certain types of crime. Perhaps that was why His Lordship had limited it to business capital, Ulen thought, after he had sentenced an arrogant young man known to the police as The Itch to twenty-five years for a string of hold-ups at the point of a gun. The Itch had snarled at him when he turned to leave the bar, but Ulen felt that he was not sentencing him for one crime but for a bad life, for which the young man may not have been wholly responsible. He would have preferred sentencing him in such a way that The Itch might have emerged from prison after a year, had it been possible to rehabilitate him so soon; or never, had it not been possible. Ulen did not believe that he was protecting society by handing out pat numbers of years that might or might not coincide with a reasonable kind of regeneration. Severe sentences, including that of death, were an admission that society had no idea of what to do with its malefactors and after having enjoyed the thrill of vengeance did not wish to be bothered.

Only infrequently could he reach into the stream of cases and add something of his own. For the most part he had to be content with being an umpire, but now and then he had chances. He looked up from noting his disposition of The Itch in his docket and saw two young men being arraigned.[1] They were without counsel and pleaded not guilty. It was mid-afternoon and there were no lawyers in court. Ulen rubbed his chin and reflected. Charles Hanker and Harry Bring; the charge was obtaining money under false pretenses, issuing worthless checks, conspiracy to cheat and defraud, assault and battery. Dalling, the deputy District Attorney, came to the bench at Ulen's nod.

---

[1] The indictment, or legal statement of the criminal charge, must be read to the accused in open Court, and he must answer by saying guilty, not guilty, or unwilling to contest. If he stands mute, a plea of not guilty is entered for him. Indictments are becoming shorter and simpler, but in some places the old language is still used, and in a murder indictment the wording is quaint but takes an unconscionable amount of time to read.

"How about trying these boys without counsel?"

"I think it's all right," Dalling answered. "The case is clear; straightaway stuff and no hitches."

Ulen agreed, knowing that he could trust Dalling. In order to be sure, Ulen asked the boys if they had employed counsel, but they shook their heads. Bring stepped forwards a little when he did so, as if the initiative were on him. He was a finely built boy of about twenty-three, and quite handsome, with intelligent blue eyes and wavy blond hair. Ulen found that he had to look twice at his eyes. There was something about them, a little too wide open. They looked straight but too far, as if unfocused. The other boy, a trifle younger than his companion, was nondescript and pale, obviously frightened and pliable.

The trial took about an hour. Two hotel detectives testified, and several policemen who had supervised the confession that both boys had made soon after their arrest. One of the officers had a cut above one eye.

The story was a simple one. The boys had met in prison in a neighboring State and had planned to meet at Hanker's room after their release. There they were to get some papers of Hanker's showing that he had worked for a short time in a commercial establishment. Bring, who was the leader in the venture, was to take Hanker's name and Hanker was to assume an alias. Then they planned to work their way about the country in a leisurely fashion, stopping at hotels for a fortnight or so and paying with checks drawn on Hanker's former employer. He recalled the name of the official who had signed his paychecks, and the name of the bank.

This plan they proceeded to carry out. They were able to

identify themselves at hotels by altering the company's papers and bringing them up to date, and by having checks printed to look like the company's checks. Their first move had been to go to the nearby city where the company was located and get a checkbook from its bank. After cashing their first check they bought a salesman's sample bag, put a few bricks in it wrapped in newspapers, and carried it about for the sake of appearances. After enjoying themselves thoroughly for three months they were apprehended, having spent about six hundred dollars of the company's money. They surrendered readily enough, but while they were being put in the patrol wagon Bring took offense at an off-hand remark made by one of the officers and punched him in the eye. He did not, however, try to escape.

It was a run of mine story but there were things about it that made Ulen prick up his ears. Bring had apparently dominated Hanker to the point where the younger boy did whatever the other told him to do. Hanker's confession revealed that at one time he had tried to rebel, but that Bring had beaten him and thereafter refused to let him out of his sight, on threat of giving him up to the police. Hanker could not go alone even to get his hair cut. It also appeared that Bring cashed his checks during the first few days of their visit to a hotel, instead of at the end, when it was time to pay. They had confessed voluntarily, without persuasion. And they had left a wide trail behind them while moving from city to city. It was as if they wanted to be caught. No, not they, only Bring. The other had taken fright and had tried to get away when he had his tussle with Bring. Odd. It might be a text-book case after all. He'd think about it over night.

After the State rested, Bring took the stand and admitted the whole story. Dalling looked at him reflectively.

"Why didn't you plead guilty, if you admit the charges?" he asked.

Bring shuffled his feet.

"Well, I didn't know," he said. "I didn't have no lawyer."

Ulen glanced at the record of the boy's previous criminal record and pursed his lips.

"Well, all right," Dalling said with a slight shrug of his shoulders. "That's all."

Hanker followed suit, but with suppressed rebellion. He probably felt that he was caught and would get off easier if he didn't put up a fight.

Ulen instructed the jury briefly that both defendants had admitted the charges but that it was for the jury to weigh the evidence as carefully as in any other case. The foreman took the bills of indictment in his hand and arose to visit his fellow jurors in the box. He was a tired little man, and his trousers, which were unpressed and slightly too large for him, hung down behind him like wet curtains in the rain. Ulen watched him idly. Much can be gleaned about personality, he found himself observing, from the seat of a man's pants. The foreman returned and nodded to the bailiff. The jury had agreed at once that both defendants were guilty on all counts.

"Well, there isn't much doubt about that," Ulen said to them, "but there are some aspects of this case that interest me when it comes to passing sentence. I want to think about them over night. I'll sentence in the morning."

When court opened the next day the boys were not at the defendants' table. There had been a delay in getting them down in the van from prison. The jury took their places in the box, ready for new cases. The clock ticked loudly. Ulen wondered how he might improve the idle moment. Well, if his theory of the case was sound he ought to be willing to make it public; he had determined to act on it anyway. He turned to the jury.

"Ladies and gentlemen," he said, "before the defendants get here I'd like to tell you how I look at this case. Your duty couldn't have been easier; the facts were clear and the boys admitted them. My job is very much harder, for I don't want to clap these boys into jail without some idea of what I'm doing. My first difficulty lies in the different criminal records they have, and that means I must treat them differently and make each feel that the difference is fair." He paused and picked up the record cards.

"Hanker has been arrested only once before," he went on, "a minor offense for which he was serving a short sentence when he met Bring. Most likely I'll put him on probation, for if he can fall so easily under another boy's domination, as he has done already in prison, it would be folly to put him in the same position again.

"Bring has been arrested thirteen times for offenses similar to the one we heard yesterday. He is twenty-four years old and has spent seven years of his life in jail. I must send him back again, but for how long and under what conditions is what worries me. I think that the boy is emotionally upset. He's not insane. In fact, he's rather intelligent and I suspect he has a fairly high I. Q. But there is something wrong with a boy who follows a pattern of crime like this, who leaves a plain trail behind him without bothering very much to cover it up, who confesses freely, and who then admits his crime before a jury. It looks as if he wanted to be caught.

"As yet I don't know why. That's my job to find out from him if I can. We judges who sit here day after day are beginning to feel that boys like Bring have reasons for committing crimes and are not senselessly wicked. Unfortunately, they do not often understand the reason themselves. These reasons lie hidden in their past, and if it is possible to find them and explain them, these boys may see things differently and go straight. We haven't time or facilities in court to get at the reasons properly. I shall try today but I may fail.

"My hunch is that Bring is suffering from what the doctors call the will to die. They say we all have it, together with the will to live, but in most people it is so well under control that only in moments of great trouble does it rise to bother them, usually in the form of discouragement or boredom. We've all had moments when we'd like to give up and don't care whether school keeps or not. That's the will to die. In a few people it is so strong that they commit suicide. In others it is less strong but it is still so much in control of them that it affects their lives for the worse. These are the people who always seem to have bad luck, who get injured frequently, who look on the dark side of things, or who repeat a certain pattern of crime. Very often they actually want to be punished, as if the better part of them were trying to atone for what the worse part of them made them do. They think that it's an honorable and manly way of starting a new life. It's really a tragic aspect of the hidden conflict within them that goes on and on, driving them in an endless circle to new crimes and new confessions.

"Here they come. Follow my questions if you are interested, and if you think of anything you would like to ask the boys yourselves, please feel free to do so. I shall need all the help I can get."

Ulen called on Hanker first and questioned him closely about his futile revolt against his companion. Hanker had nothing to add to his confession; Bring had set upon him with unexpected ferocity and had not let him out of his sight thereafter. Ulen dismissed him and asked Bring to stand up. The boy did so, facing the bench calmly and with determination.

"Well," Ulen remarked, picking up the card again and reading it aloud, "that's a pretty long record, isn't it?"

"It is, sir," Bring replied.

"It's correct, is it?"

"It is, sir."

"You were first arrested when you were fourteen?"

"I was, sir."

"What was done with you then?"

"I was put on probation, sir. I wanted to be sent to a Home."

"Oh, you wanted to be sent to a Home," Ulen repeated and paused. "What do you think I should do to you now?"

"I think I should be punished, sir."

"And why?"

"Because I have done wrong, sir."

"Well, now," Ulen said encouragingly, "you must have known that this was wrong to do before you did it." He raised his eyebrows in question.

"Yes, sir."

Ulen omitted asking him why he had done it then. It was an idiotic question, for no one ever knew.

"And you must have known each time you were arrested that you had done wrong. Did you do this, by any chance, in order to be punished?"

Bring shot a startled glance at Ulen and gave a slight laugh.

"Oh no, sir," he said.

Ulen gazed at the ceiling for a moment.

"Well," he went on, "you don't know why you did this, so I won't ask you. But let's see if we can find out. You say you wanted to be sent to a Home ten years ago. Didn't you have a home?"

"My mother died that year," Bring said.

"How did you get along with your father?"

"All right."

"How did you get along with your mother?"

"All right."

Ulen paused. He didn't feel that he was getting very far. He'd have to try a few shots in the dark.

"Was your father a big man?" he asked.

"Yes, sir."

"And strong?"

"Very strong."

"Was your mother strong too?"

"No, sir, she was sickly like."

"What did your father do for a living?"

Bring looked down. "He didn't do nothing for a long time. He used to drive a truck but lost his job and couldn't get another."

"How did you all live?"

"Mother took in washing."

"And couldn't stand it, is that right?"

"That, and pop's fighting with her. He didn't never hit her but I think he killed her, the things he said to her." There was a slight flush in his cheeks.

Ulen leaned back. Getting warm. Must go carefully. As he was planning his next questions, Juror No. 3 arose and held up her hand. She was a small woman with professional eyeglasses.

"May I ask a question?" she inquired timidly. Ulen nodded.

"Did you have any brothers or sisters?" she asked, turning to Bring.

The boy looked around hastily to locate his questioner. He glanced at Ulen as if for permission and then addressed her directly.

"I had a brother," he replied.

"Had or have?" she inquired.

"I guess he's still around somewhere. I haven't seen him for a long time."

"Was he younger than you?"

"Yes, m'am."

Juror No. 3 murmured: "Thank you," and sat down. Ulen looked at her with a twinkle, which she returned. He resumed his questioning.

"Did your father ever give you any money?" he asked directly.

"Not a cent." The answer shot out with venom.

"How did he treat you?"

"He picked on me all the time, same as he did on mother. There wasn't nothing I could do right."

"And how did he treat your brother?"

"Altogether different. There wasn't nothing the kid could do wrong."

Ulen got up and walked back and forth a few times behind his chair. He felt elated. It rarely came out as clearly as this. How to make the boy see it was the next problem. He came back and sat down, leaning forward eagerly.

"I think we've gotten somewhere," he said. "Listen carefully and see if you agree with what I say now.

"You loved your mother and hated your father. He was unkind to her and to you. You also hated your brother because he was younger and your father favored him. Is that right so far?"

Bring looked startled.

"I don't know, sir," he said, a trifle mechanically.

"Think about it," said Ulen. "Think about this too.

"When you first broke the law and were arrested, shortly after your mother's death, you were really trying to get away from your father. You wanted to be sent to a Home, but they put you on probation because it was your first offense. It was the worst thing they could have done to you. So you broke the law again and finally were sent to jail, as you wanted.

"When this case came up you were playing the old game that has now become a habit. You got a younger man and made him do what you wanted. In that way you got back at your brother. Then you played the hotels, which are a kind of home. You went to good ones, in order to get money for the asking from well-dressed men whom you wished your father had resembled. By cheating them you were cheating your father and getting the money he never gave you. The policeman also stood in the position of your father and when he said something you didn't like you poked him in the eye. Now you want to be punished, partly to escape from your father again and partly to make up to your conscience for having done wrong.

"You're still fighting your father and your brother and you'll do it the rest of your life unless you realize it.

"Does that make any sense to you at all?"

Bring simply looked bewildered.

"I don't know, sir," he repeated, sullenly.

"I'm not surprised you don't know," Ulen went on. "It takes time. I must send you to jail again so you can have the time. If I let you go you'd commit a worse offense in order to be sure your conscience would be satisfied. I shall send you a typewritten copy of what I have been saying and you can look it over.

"You are twenty-four years old. It's time you forgot your brother and your father and stood on your own feet. You're being haunted by their ghosts.

"It is better to give you the punishment you want, so you can think it over and perhaps shake yourself free from the past. I'll give you two years in the County prison."

He put Hanker on probation.

"I won't send you back to get tied up to somebody else who might be worse for you," he commented. "But the probation will be strict. You need help too and I'll see to it that your probation means real guidance."

The boys filed out and Ulen turned again to the jury.

"It seemed to work out," he remarked. "But whether he comes to a full realization of it himself is another matter.

People are scared to death in court. I'm sure I'd be if I sat down there.

"I'll instruct the warden of the County prison to report Bring's progress to me. If he is a model prisoner I will keep him there, for that will mean that he has learned nothing. If he starts raising hell in jail and breaking the rules I'll let him out on parole at once for the rest of his term. It would be the surest indication that he has come to his senses and wants to make a new start. Actions and reactions usually balance, and I'll be overjoyed if he causes the warden a lot of trouble."

The voice came from nearby and the telephone sounded as if there were sea-shells in it. It was Judge Brennan. "Oh, Ulen," he said, "I've just appointed a new bailiff and now I wish I hadn't. He's been giving me trouble. Fellow named Paltrey. Seems to regard witnesses as a special diet recommended by the doctor. I've tried to break him in up here in civil court but it isn't working out. I want to give him one more chance, and criminal court is the only place to do it. He'll be away from me and more on his own. If there should be an opening for a left hook, you'll be serving your city; put a horseshoe in your glove. Do you mind?" Ulen gave assurance that he did not and Brennan hung up.

When he got to court the next morning he kept an eye on the new bailiff. His colleague had not overdrawn the picture. The man bullied the witnesses and herded them about like cattle. While the arraignments and guilty pleas were being disposed of, Ulen became indignant, for the public at the rear of the jury room was taking notice.

The first case for the jury involved four boys, about seventeen years old, charged with malicious mischief. They sat behind their counsel with the air of subdued concern common to the very young who are dangerously innocent of criminal intent. The prosecutor was also a young man, and when Paltrey barked his name he came slowly forwards and sat down in the witness chair. He was very slight and had a mild but wary eye.

"On your feet!" shouted Paltrey.

The young man did not move.

"Stand up," roared Paltrey. "You want to swear, don't you?" The young man took his time but arose.

"I do," he said. "To hell with you."

There was a snirt of laughter from the courtroom. Ulen rapped for order but made no other sign. "Swear the witness," he said brusquely. Paltrey's face was red but he opened the Bible.

"Put your right hand on the Book," he ordered. The witness did not move. Paltrey repeated the command savagely.

The young man regarded him coolly.

"I'm left-handed," he remarked.

Paltrey flinched for a short second and turned to Ulen. For all he knew, there might be a law about it.

"The witness says he's left-handed, Your Honor," he announced bleakly.

Ulen did not hesitate.

"So I heard," he observed. "The customer, Mr. Paltrey, is always right. Go and get him a left-handed Bible at once."

Paltrey did not hesitate either. "Yes, sir," he said and strode from the room.

The young man turned an apologetic eye towards the

bench. "Sorry, Your Honor," he said in a low voice, "but I thought he had it comin' to 'im."

Ulen raised an absolving eyebrow and swore the young man himself. The trial did not take long, for the case was simple, and no one in the courtroom was in much doubt of the outcome or of the imponderables, which, paradoxically enough, always determine the weight and strain of a crime upon the social fabric. The jury readily convicted, but recommended mercy.

The facts were an example of the collective ingenuity of four precocious intelligences with nothing better to do. They had conceived the idea of making forays late at night, armed with saws and axes, into the back roads where hapless couples in parked cars, unaware of treachery, were pleasantly passing the evening under the curtain of the overhanging woods. The boys selected a car and divided their forces, two going into the woods ahead of the car and two behind it. Each group then attacked a tree, and when the upper branches began to shiver, they guided its fall athwart the road with blood-curdling cries of: "Timber!" They synchronized their efforts carefully in order that both trees might fall together and effectively barricade the car.

While the boys were working on the prosecutor's car, however, he moved it ahead a little in order to avoid an inconvenient slope in the highway, but the boys were too busy with their trees to notice that he had changed his position. Had he not climbed into the back seat by the time the tree fell, he might have been seriously injured by the ragged stump of a branch that struck like a fist out of the darkness and hung quivering a foot above the driver's seat. The car, whose top was down, was badly scratched but otherwise unharmed. When the boys returned to their own car, the police, who had been guided there by frantic pleas for help on previous evenings, were waiting for them.

Man's incongruous innocence, Ulen said to himself.

Such ingenuity should be encouraged, but it needed trimming. A criminal record of malicious mischief for hacking down a few trees would not harm them in later life, but jail would never do; a night in the police station, preceding the entry of bail, had been enough of that. The boys were standing at the bar now, their families grouped anxiously behind them. He asked the boys how they liked humiliating their people by bringing them to court, and one of them started to blubber. His father put a stiff arm around his shoulder and looked hard at Ulen. The mother began fishing for her handkerchief.

Ulen let them stew. He wasn't going to hurt them, but they didn't know it, and he couldn't make it too easy. He hated playing cat and mouse with them, but it was one of the few effective things that court procedure made possible. A poor device, he thought, and grunted.

There was a bustle at the rear door. Paltrey was making his way through the crowd, holding a book in one hand. There was a glucose look of triumph on his face. He came forward to the bench and handed up the book. Ulen glanced at it. It was a Hebrew Bible and began at the back. He smiled slightly and leaned forward to address the defendants.

"I shall not send you to jail," he announced evenly, "but somehow you must get the idea that death can be a sober and an ugly thing. This man might have been killed or seriously injured by what you did. Your punishment will be somewhat unpleasant, but it is the best available.

"At nine o'clock tomorrow morning you shall report to the City General Hospital for a detailed tour of that institution, including the morgue, the pickling vats, and the dissecting room. I will see to it that you are admitted. Thereafter you will be on probation for a year." He paused.

"Mr. Paltrey," he continued, "will be in personal charge of the tour, so I may know that my instructions have been carried out. I will explain his absence, in detail, to Judge Brennan tomorrow, and I hope that in this way the left hand may become aware of what it is the right hand doeth."

When Ulen left his office for the day, he saw a little man walking up and down in the corridor, thoughtfully smoking his pipe. He had come to know the little man's face well but he did not know his name. No one did, and no one knew where he came from, for he appeared at the courthouse each day as if the tide of the city had cast him there and would take him with it again when it ebbed in the evening. He appeared to have no will of his own in the matter and no visible means of support, for he spent the day visiting various courtrooms or walking pensively in the corridors with his pipe. On rare occasions he spoke to people, but he stuttered so badly that conversation was a burden on both sides. The effort to get the words out caused him to open his mouth slowly, until it was as wide as he could get it, and at that point he usually broke off with as much of a grin as he could manage under the circumstances, putting his head on one side and shaking it vigorously up and down, as if the whole affair were too deep for words and its meaning inescapable. At the same time he jabbed at his listener with the stem of his pipe and grew redder and redder in the face.

It is likely that this confusion at the gateway of speech had caused the words that struggled within him to back up against his brain and soften it. When he was able to unleash an articulate idea, it became apparent that he had worked so hard to make it simple and pointed, in order to get it out at all, that the process of refining it had whittled away whatever sense it had had to begin with. For the most part he had given up speaking altogether and was content to sit in court and listen to people who could. As a member of the public, he had the right to go to court if he wanted to, and he felt that he was being addressed, in a derivative sort of way, without having to make any response. Otherwise people were too impatient, and he might have lived in complete loneliness if it had not been for his right to be an unofficial juror.

His habit of visiting the courts had begun some years ago after he had once been called on a panel, and he had appeared every morning fifteen minutes early, his threadbare clothes carefully brushed and the long hairs at the side of his head plastered neatly over his crown. He had been chosen for the first case, which happened to be an important one, but when the jury was polled [2] at the end of the trial and he had to stand

[2] Not an outing on the river. There are times when counsel cannot believe his ears when he hears the verdict, and sometimes cases are sufficiently complicated to warrant the suspicion that the jury may not have understood or may not actually have agreed but were willing to let the foreman handle everything. Counsel for either party has the right to ask that the jury be polled. Each juryman then arises and announces the verdict, if he can, and woe betide the case in which there are inconsistent answers or a juror looks stupid and says he doesn't know. The masculine pronoun includes the feminine.

up alone and announce his findings, he was utterly unable to do so. Thereafter the clerk hadn't been able to find the strip that had his name on it in the jury wheel. He continued to arrive early each morning, however, and he leaned forward eagerly whenever a new jury was being chosen, his eyes on the clerk's face and his hands on the arms of his chair so that he could get up quickly without having to answer to his name. When the twelve jurors had been chosen without him, he sat back again and passed his hand over his mouth, but he followed each case with minute attention and appeared to make up his mind about it, on the chance that he might be asked. After his two weeks of service were over, he continued coming to court as a spectator, with the air of a man who has retired and can enjoy life at his leisure. He often came late, for he knew just what to do: opening the door, he politely removed his hat with one hand and his pipe with the other, and made directly for the last row of chairs in the public's section of the room. He walked down the center aisle, knowing his rights and savoring the journey a little, and paused for a moment to survey the scene before taking careful possession of a chair. When court recessed for lunch, he went out and sat on one of the benches in the corridor to eat his lunch, which consisted invariably of an apple and a bottle of soft drink. After he had slowly dispatched these and had hidden the core and the empty bottle behind the bench, he lighted his pipe and wandered along the deserted corridors until time for court to reconvene. He then waited until the judge had appeared on the bench and a bailiff had closed the courtroom door. Smiling vacantly to himself, he tamped down the tobacco in his pipe, opened the door, and made his entrance.

He had the habit of visiting the same courtroom for two or three months at a time, and Ulen often wondered what he made out of the cases that he listened to so carefully. The little man had a way of getting particularly interested at the oddest moments, and Ulen and his colleagues began to refer to him as the little man who glowed. At these times he slowly got very red in the face and heaved with suppressed amusement. This rarely coincided with the exciting parts of a trial, which may have been too much for him, for they caused him simply to stare straight ahead of him and put his chin on top of his fist. But given two or three hours of cross-examining an accountant on items of inventory or a doctor explaining the technical difficulties of a fractured malleolus, the little man would begin to glow happily.

As time went on, he gathered enough courage to speak to Ulen after a case was over. He had a curious ability to know when someone was not in a hurry, and Ulen was able to be patient with him. That was barely enough, for the little man's mental processes were so peculiar that Ulen couldn't divine where his ideas were going and find ways to help him out. By degrees, however, he discovered that the little man's culture consisted of a single historical fact and that all of his observations were related to it. This fact was that Abraham Lincoln had been shot in a place called Ford's Theater. Ulen made the discovery after finishing a long accident case in which a man had been killed by a gas explosion. The little man had cornered him after the trial, jabbing at him with his pipestem and letting his pale blue eyes walk up Ulen's face from the chin. What with the gas going off like that, he had managed to observe at length, it was like that proposition at Ford's

Theater. Yes, yes, it was, Ulen had said brightly, indeed it was; and the little man had gone off satisfied, nodding his head carefully and getting his mouth closed again. Gas – explosion – gun – Ford's Theater, Ulen had muttered to himself, trying to piece it together and not feeling that he had got hold of very much. But it had come out the next day, while he was hearing a tax assessment case. The real estate experts were particularly dull, listing their sales and trying to explain corner influence. In the depths of it the little man had begun to glow. Hello, said Ulen to himself, I guess the Theater's being assessed or sold or something. He never did find out quite what it was, for while the little man approached him again, the pipestem was having unusual difficulty that day and all that Ulen could gather was that them tax cases were like that prop – before the little man had to give up and nod the rest of it across the chasm.

After that he disappeared abruptly and Ulen missed him. Several months later he received a note written in an almost illegible hand on the stationery of the City Hospital. It was unsigned and read: "they have me here in sity hospitle like that propasiton when pres. linken was shot in ford theter i don no why except that i understan about cases but i am all rite an i want you to help me get out."

Ulen frowned and made inquiries. It was not long before he was referred to Dr. Malker, a psychiatrist to whom the judges often referred cases of dubious normality. She was an intelligent creature, and with considerable color she gave Ulen an account of what had happened.

The little man, after leaving Ulen's court, had decided to visit some of the other judges. One of these was Judge Ringler, who was not a very strong judge and had considerable difficulty being affirmed by the appellate courts. He was sensitive about this, and with his re-election approaching he had become suspicious of nearly everyone that attended his court. After watching the little man glow at unexpected moments for a week or so, Ringler came to the conclusion that he was a political spy and that the thing to do was to take action. He halted the trial that he was conducting at a moment when the little man had grown a brick red, and ordered him from the courtroom. The little man, hurt and astonished, made for the door as fast as he could and prowled unhappily about the corridors. Hearing something that led him to believe that Ringler would not be there the next day, he reached the courtroom early and sat as far back among the spectators as he could. To his dismay, Ringler appeared and court opened. Ringler also noticed with dismay that the little man was there again, trying to hide himself. He halted the trial and had him ejected by a bailiff. Before the little man could ask what he had done, the bailiff had closed the door in his face. He walked up and down for a long time, thinking hard, but he couldn't come to any conclusion about it and decided that he'd find out direct from the judge. After all, he had once served on a jury and he knew about cases. He had a right to be there, but maybe there was some law about it and he'd better find out. He'd have to be careful and not violate any laws; coming to court had made life bearable. If he couldn't come any more he didn't know what he'd do.

He was standing outside Ringler's office when court recessed for lunch. Suddenly the door opened and Ringler appeared, accompanied by a young woman. He was talking to her earnestly and had thrown one arm lightly around her shoulder. It struck the little man as funny to see the judge standing there in the corridor with his arm around a woman. He began to grow warm and pink, and an idea struck him. He took his pipe from his mouth and pointed it at Ringler while he moved towards him, trying to get it clear and straight. He had to get this out so it could be understood, and he tested his tongue against the roof of his mouth while the warm humor rose in him. The judge raised his eyes and looked at him with sudden distaste, but it was too late to get away and he watched the accusing pipestem draw nearer. It was almost at his chest now and the man was opening his mouth like an idiot. No question the fellow was trying to get something on him. He slid his arm from the girl's shoulder and glared. No use trying to act stupid, I know what you're up to, he was thinking. The little man was burbling in spite of himself under the impulse of the comical idea, but he felt control coming. Just a few words: the judge would roar when he saw the joke, and everything would be all right so that he could come to court again. He gave one desperate lunge with the pipestem at the judge's arm while the idea boiled in his head.

"Is that l-l-l-legal?" he said.

He had got it out well. He stood with his mouth open and his head bobbing while he fastened his eyes with anxious confidence on the judge's face. He was helping him to have fun over it: when the judge saw the point he'd laugh. Just give him a minute and grin at him. But the minute grew until it was out of shape, and Ringler's face hardened. He motioned to the bailiff.

"Take this man over to Dr. Malker," he said, brushing his

hands slowly together. "Tell her I want a report in the morning."

The little man tried to explain the funny thing he had said, but the words wouldn't come and the situation seemed to have got tangled up. The bailiff was hurrying him along the corridor, and he was sitting in a cell before he knew what was happening to him.

Dr. Malker examined him late that afternoon, and next morning she sent Ringler a report that the prisoner was slightly feeble-minded but quite harmless. But Ringler had already directed his law clerk to make out commitment papers, and when they were ready he looked at them for a moment hesitantly. Might be a question of legality about this, but by the time it could be straightened out, the election would be over and it wouldn't matter. Besides, the law clerk hadn't raised any question and had gone to all this trouble. He took up the pen and scratched his name angrily.

Ulen called on Ringler and was as tactful as possible. He pointed out that a man couldn't be committed quite so abruptly, and added that he knew the little man and could answer for him. Ringler, his chin on his chest, blustered but finally gave in and signed an order of release. Ulen made sure that the little man was discharged, but after that he disappeared, and when Ulen investigated the address that he had given to the police and the hospital, it turned out to be an abandoned warehouse. Neither Ulen nor any of the other judges ever saw him again.

VIII

Jon and Sara Sander

SARA SANDER left home when she was a lithe and precocious young lady of seventeen. The reasons for her leaving and for her precocity were not obscure. She was the third in age of four children. Her older sisters played no part in her subsequent story, for one of them was already married to a man who qualified in every way for the ambitions that her parents had for her, and the other was engaged to a boy whose brilliance compensated for his lack of social position. Sara was therefore expendable, from the dynastic point of view.

The youngest of the Sander children was a boy, two years Sara's junior, and all of his parents' hopes centered in him. Sara was skipped over, largely because she had a mind of her own and an annoying way of challenging her parents' positions on things that they affected to take for granted because they were knotty and could be skirted or excluded altogether. Sara, accepting the world as she found it, skirted nothing, but went headlong into whatever she met. She wanted to know what being poor meant, and being nice, and why she couldn't ask to supper certain gentle and intriguing young things of her own age who lived down the road and had dark brown skins. She was not content to be told that some day she would understand and meanwhile must accept the view that all people should know their place and stay in it.

This had occurred when Sara was about seven, and she didn't understand it. She had cornered her father with the question while he stood before the fire, steaming comfortably after a horseback ride through the woods on an incandescent Sunday in October. Mr. Sander, hands behind him and rocking from heel to toe, surveyed his daughter as he would a porcupine which had suddenly appeared in the middle of his living-room. The long ride, the flow of horseflesh beneath him, the dry mutter and creak of leather, and the cool burn of the wind on his face, gave him a sense of empire whose reach was self-sustaining. His own natural wariness and his firmness of character could protect it against all enemies, foreign and domestic. He looked at his feet with a quick frown while Sara faced him, legs wide apart, and told him about the new friends she had made. It struck him with sharp discomfort as being one of those problems that he had settled for himself long ago and therefore felt that he had also settled for his family without having to say anything about it. He resented Sara's raising it. Why couldn't she look about her and see that it had no place in the life he had created for her? She was a difficult child, asking questions no one should ask who had been brought up as she had been.

She stood looking at him squarely. Getting to know things was as natural as breathing, and her firm young face demanded her rights. She wanted to know more about her new friends and about the exciting difference between them and herself, but from above came the familiar voice of doom.

"No," it said shortly, "you can't have them in to supper. They're not our kind, that's all. Some day you will understand. Meanwhile don't ask questions."

It was not her way to argue. She had learned that it got her nowhere. Her father's gaze simply became glassy. He repeated what he had said and moved off on a pressing errand. She turned and gazed out of the large window at the sloping lawn and the flat button of a pond in the distance. She would have to find out for herself about these children with the funny skin. She was not angry with her father, for she knew that he would not follow the point beyond blocking her request. He had little time for her, and she knew that he thought of her only when she was under his eye. She was free to come and go as she pleased, and she had learned only too well how to get around her parents' injunctions. Being adept at this technique themselves, it was the one thing they had taught her more thoroughly than if they had done it consciously. In a way she did not dislike her father. Both were firm and solitary, and at the rare moments when they happened upon each other in the garden or in the woods they struck a remote but common chord, as if they had heard the echo of the same bell afar off. Wrapped in themselves, they failed to explore together the intervening distance and were content to go their own ways, indifferent but not actively hostile to each other.

Mr. Sander, like all men that marry elfin women and bring them to the large institution they think of as home, had found that the weight of its principal responsibilities fell on him. He managed the farm and grounds and paid the servants. The kitchen and the children he left to his wife. His part was to supply the plant and keep it running. The rest was women's work and it should be done automatically, without invading his province. The result was that they rarely met, except at meals, where the shock of being alone together was usually relieved by the presence of company. Mr. Sander also had his brokerage business to attend to, and his clubs.

Mrs. Sander was a frail woman with a large pair of vague but beautiful eyes and a tongue to match. It was as if her body had been born into the world and her head into a separate and special kind of fairyland. Her favorite line of poetry was, "the horns of elfland faintly blowing," and it became the background of her whole approach to the world. She accepted life with joy. The horrible, the grotesque, and the cruel existed for her only as beauty in misshapen form to give color to the wondrous scene in which she lived. All creatures and things were uniformly good, and she spoke to them or about them as if they were people and endowed with sentient and responsive life. She was well-read and intelligent, save for the twist in her that transmuted everything into a fairylike beauty not born of religious ecstasy so much as existing in a phantasmal world of sheer gossamer. There was room in her world for dragons and giants and witches, but they existed only to be exorcised by a smile or a touch of whimsey. When she ran against evil too stubborn to budge out of her path, she turned aside from it with a little indrawn hiss and closed her eyes dramatically.

"Oh, I know there's evil," she once said, clasping her hands and gazing at the distant trees. "It's terrible to think that people – I'm sure they don't, not really."

She rarely finished her sentences or connected them. Too many good fairies crowded forward for expression, and behind each one there was such an ineffable light that until the little darlings were all attended to there was no going on. Her preoccupation with this shining world within her made her vague in her relations with the world around her. She spent hours in her garden, and her flowers were famous. "They are only the heads of my dears," she said, looking crestfallen at the idea that there were struggling bodies beneath the soil and that she was incapable of releasing them. "They want – Sara, hand me – it *is* Tuesday, isn't it? Tuesday is the day for snapdragons, isn't it, darlings?"

Her children grew up a great deal more casually than her flowers. She was unable to meet any actual problem head on. She curved and bent around it, not solving it but stimulating it by a variety of oblique thrusts to solve itself. Most often her problems did solve themselves very well, for she had considerable insight in dealing with good and directing it; evil and sheer strength, however, were beyond her power of handling. Sara writhed under her mother's indirection and had more trouble in evading her evasiveness than she had in steering a clear course around the blunt obstacles that her father put in her way. She saw that her mother's affection for her was diffuse, a wind that blew around her but never straight upon her, and it made her feel that she was only a symbol for some real fairy that her mother saw in her. As a little girl, she had pretended to be that fairy, and instantly her mother had grown clear and single, and the gap between them had closed. Later the rôle became too unreal to sustain and Sara gave it up. Mrs. Sander was intelligent enough to know it. "She has drifted off on a moonbeam of her own," she said once to a friend, capable of complete speech only when her thought was evanescent. Having stated the fact, she let Sara drift away on whatever kind of moonbeam it might be, since it was part of her own aerial life to believe that everyone else's was as lovely as hers and that thwarting it might distort it. No one told her that she lived in a fool's paradise. Mr. Sander, to whom all imagination was madness except when it applied to business and was then called vision or sound judgment, was vaguely irritated by her tenuous hold on the factual processes of life and put the rest down to charm. Mrs. Sander's experience had taught her that it was best to muffle her whimsey a little in his presence, and their friends, who were so extroverted that they were bored without knowing it by the ceaseless impact of practical situations upon them, found her confusingly delicious and said so. He was happy to accept their judgment of her. Fantasy is a bewildering poison to very male men and women.

Sara and her mother rapidly grew apart, there being little to hold them together. Even the child's growing interest in modelling failed to stem the drift, for Mrs. Sander's sprites were too fluid to interest her when cast in enduring immobility. Sara saw the world in solid pieces. The banked trees beyond the pond or a block of clouds were masses that she wanted to preserve long before she thought of heads and bodies, and her early efforts with clay were difficult to follow. She was not given to explaining unless asked, and she was rarely asked. Once her mother passed by and drooped above her for a moment, looking down with a puzzled smile at the rounded handfuls of wet clay resting fatly on the board before her daughter.

"What is it, darling?" Mrs. Sander lifted her voice to a little squeak at the end, unaware that a real question rides along on the level and finally jumps down to face its object squarely.

"Clouds," Sara answered briefly.

Mrs. Sander clucked gaily and leaned forward, pinching the clay with her long, deft fingers. "It should have a face," she said, cocking her head on one side. "There. A dear little face. Now it's a somebody."

Sara looked at it coldly. "Clouds don't have faces," she said.

"Mine do," her mother replied. "But you must have a teacher, darling. Your father – oh, I know it'll be." She went off, giving Sara two tiny pats on the top of her head.

So Mrs. Sander bolted that door between them. A teacher came promptly, for it was the Sanders' habit, when they did think of something their children needed, to find someone else to provide it. In this way the children grew up among hired enthusiasms and came to regard most of them with a compensating indifference. Fortunately for Sara, her tutor was a lively and comprehending young man who caught eagerly at her spark of originality and warmed it with his own. By the time she was fifteen he had taught her all he knew. He was severe with her technique and lenient with whatever it was that she wanted to express by it, and by the time he left he had not only established her talent but had made her aware of it. He had, in short, fashioned her freedom and put it in her hands.

Her only other real companion was her younger brother Jon. The boy was a fairly even mixture of his father and mother. He stood between them and received their adoration equably; yet he was able to balance it by the touch of suppressed resentment of each other that he had inherited from them both. He was male enough to value the comfortable advantages of his position and so young that he could catch the hidden false notes and make them mercilessly vocal. In her loneliness Sara was a willing sounding-board for him, but she was too single in her growing artistic development to make a return in kind. She did not destroy, by competing with it, his pleasure in making fun of his parents. It was to her interest to let it develop. She even stimulated it by sharing with him a trick of observation that her tutor had taught her. What you must do, he had told her in effect, is to slice movement at the precise point of its greatest significance and sculpture the raw cross-section just as you see it. Choose what mood or emotion you want and wait for it, but when it comes catch it at its exact pinnacle and don't let go.

She and Jon made a game of it at table. They studied their parents and older sisters after deciding in advance what they would look for. Throughout the meal they would watch with barely repressed excitement, their eyes fastened like gimlets on their victim. The game was to see how nearly they agreed, and when they thought the critical instant had arrived they would cry: "Slice!" In many things they would hit upon the split second together, as in the case of Mr. Sander's peculiar sneeze; the point was to catch him at the quintessential instant when his lungs had reached their capacity of breath and his pre-concussional bliss was at its most exquisite. Holding their own breath while their father soared up the slope of this delicious agony, they hung with him on the crest until they dared no longer, and sliced. "No fair after his head bobs," Jon had ruled. In other things agreement came less easily – "when Mother sees a pixie," was Sara's favorite – for here there was room for interpretation and comparison.

They taught themselves to observe, coldly and with devastating accuracy. Sara's intent gray eyes grew colder and more intent when an emotional crisis swept over the family. The more personal it was the more impersonal she became. Her sisters often flew into frenzies over something or other, and her mother fluttered around the edges of the storm like a bird in a gale. Sara's eyes shot from one to the other. Helen's mouth grew ugly when she was angry. Sara measured the distance the lower lip drooped and the effect it had of smoothing out two small creases on either side of the nose. She noted the hunch of Helen's thin shoulders and their rounding into balls when they came forwards, like supporting artillery. Mrs. Sander seemed to rise a little in her chair when she was excited, and her hands scattered upwards, as if she had called on all of her fairies to keep her up and on a few of her giants to hold her down. Mr. Sander said nothing but sank lower in his chair; his bulk telescoped slightly upon itself and bulged into folds against his clothes. He gritted his teeth, and the sudden knotting of the jaw muscles made his face square and cruel.

Sara went to her studio as quickly as she could after such a tempest whenever she had noticed a new attitude of interest to her, and the room was peopled with small statues in various poses of rage and exasperation. No one ever came there but Jon. He once urged her to do a few studies of the family in mirth, but Sara wasn't interested. She felt that laughter was too often insincere and hid too much. Anger was bare and honest, like crossed swords.

Not until she was much older did she realize why laughter is so rare in sculpture. Humor creates a sudden vacuum that upsets one's flow of ideas and opinions and formulations, and sucks them into the gap so quickly that they are oddly jumbled. Laughter then sorts them out again and restores the balance. It is part of a dual process. The divine intoxicant of humor keeps us from evolving too rapidly by its mild threat to make us mad, for if we had no appetite for laughter we should accept the odd jumble at face value and lose our sanity. The loudest laughter comes from the most disorderly people or from those who have a whimsical appetite for disorder. The most orderly people laugh most rarely, and it is difficult to imagine a fully ordered person ever laughing at all. Perfect order would be found only in a very great saint whose inner joy was single and irradiated him fully. That could be caught in marble, but sculpture cannot easily catch the myriad-webbed texture of laughter with its opposing forces of sense and nonsense.

Sara wisely left laughter alone. To please Jon she once attempted a study of her father's harsh laugh when he was angry. It had no mirth in it and was a grimace of rage without lift from the eyes, which remained hard. She grew interested in the effort because she realized, while the clay rounded into shape under her fingers, that her father's angry laugh was merely an outward wrinkling of the skin from which the underlying skull remained aloof. When her mother laughed aloud her whole head became pliant, the skin and bones and brain all in motion and working together. Later Sara tried a few saints and discovered the gulf between smile and laughter. Her early saints were a little vacuous, for her experience had been with the jerk of skin and anatomy under the lash of anger and the choreic flush of tears. It was only after she had learned something of the sourceless suffusion of joy that her saints began to make sense, and when they did she turned again to ordinary people and emerged as an artist.

The development of Jon's powers of observation was less intense. He was not ridden by a dominating talent like Sara's, nor did he have to forge his own equipment for tolerable living, as she did. The attention that their parents withheld from her they showered on him, since he was the inheritor and the dynastic hope. That he grew up not completely corrupted by it was due in large measure to his relationship with Sara and to her shaping of his sense of humor. She had taught him to see through their parents and had helped him to build up a protective irony that kept them sufficiently at arm's length to prevent them from swallowing him. Sara particularly resented her mother's exquisite vacuity and needed Jon as an ally against her. She also needed someone to love. Her jealousy of her mother over Jon was the more deadly because she knew that she had the upper hand, and it did not soon occur to Mrs. Sander that she was engaged in a struggle with her youngest daughter for the affections of her son.

Sara held Jon because she offered him adventure. The drive of her art kept her intense and single-minded. There was always something going on inside her that she was willing to share with him, and it was like wine to the boy, whose appetite for external diversions was surfeited by his parents.

Young as she was, Sara was clever enough not to bore Jon with the technique of her modelling. Everything she did or said flowed in that direction, and she hid none of it from him except its application to her work. She allowed him to discover that for himself, and he prided himself on doing so, feeling that his appreciation of her ability was a contribution he could make to her. This was the peak of her effort to win him to her, and the finesse of it pleased her. She had first cultivated his powers of observation by making him sharpen them on the family; then she turned them upon herself and by doing so was able to give him the rudiments of discrimination.

Sara knew that she was working against time. Before long her father would decide that Jon should be sent to boarding school. It was the conventional thing to do, and he knew that his son needed wider fields than the fine estate on which he had been brought up. Running the estate gave Mr. Sander an escape from a world that he despised because subconsciously it frightened him; after it provided the income he required and an appropriate position among other men similarly situated, he had no idea of what to do with the world or with himself. Like many busy and successful men, he had no resources except those that could be purchased. He had to have an empire that he could see to rule, one that eye and ear and tongue could apprehend. Otherwise there was only the intolerable void. Few rich men walk abroad at night, for the stars make the void visible. Mr. Sander was nearing sixty, the time when the void starts coming through the walls in its slow campaign to claim the whole establishment and leave it soundless and hostile at death. He knew that Jon must take his place in the world in order to keep the empire and the dim echo of its founder alive. It had sheltered the boy for his first fifteen years, and the power of those early associations should hold him, but he must start out from it and learn to provide succession.

This was not lost on Sara. She accepted mankind easily because she had already fought some of the major battles of womankind, and she could recognize the inevitable when she saw it. She knew that the empire would be of no further use to her after Jon should leave it, and she made her plans accordingly. She would leave and make her own start; she was finishing school. If she stayed at home, her parents would provide for her until she married, and their satisfaction with her sisters' marriage and engagement had been apparent to her. It was not the kind of life she wanted. She would probably marry some day, but she saw no reason to sit around and wait for it to happen. She had outgrown her home, and with Jon's leaving, her main reason for working there would vanish. The world outside was better equipped to give her what she needed. She decided to wait until Jon was at his new school and not say anything to him until she was installed in the studio that she had already picked out for herself. Then she would write to him about it and he would understand.

She announced her decision at dinner a few nights after Jon had left. It was one of the rare evenings when both her parents were at home without company, and Sara had awaited just such an opportunity. She put down her demi-tasse.

"I'm going in town to live," she said.

Mr. Sander was thinking of something else and paid no attention. Mrs. Sander lifted her head and beamed mistily at her daughter.

"My blessed chrysanthemums are headed up beautifully," she said. "There was never – you won't miss them, will you, darling? Elise will pack you for a few days. Oh dear, it's – Mr. Aiken will want them for the show again, before I've finished looking at them."

Sara put her hand palm down on the table, her arm stiff.

"You don't understand, Mother," she said firmly. "I'm going in town to live. For good."

Mr. Sander cocked an eye.

"Don't be silly," he remarked.

Sara swung her eyes towards him from her mother's face.

"I won't be, thank you, Daddy," she said.

Mr. Sander shot a look at her as if it were the first time he had seen her that evening. His face grew heavy and his voice light.

"Young ladies of sixteen don't eat a good dinner and quietly announce that they are leaving home forever."

Sara looked from his eyes to his chin and back again. She paused, knowing that deliberation was her best weapon.

"This one does," she said at length. "Besides, I'm seventeen. I want to work."

"At what?" her father asked, and checked himself. "Oh, you mean your art?" He accented the word a trifle indelicately. "What does that amount to?"

Sara smiled at him.

"I'm not surprised you ask," she said. "You've never bothered to find out for yourself."

"Sara!" Mrs. Sander looked as if one of her chrysanthemums had grown a pair of legs and were walking off.

"Neither have you, Mother," Sara returned with asperity, in spite of herself. "It amounts, as you put it, Daddy, to this: I'm going to be a professional artist. I've gone as far as I can at home and I've got to move on."

Mr. and Mrs. Sander looked at each other. They were bewildered, not having built up the kind of past capable of meeting such a situation, and they suddenly realized that they had no help to give each other. Mr. Sander fell back on habit. He lighted his cigar and pushed back his chair. The girl had always been moody. This was women's work; he'd just put his foot down, and they could iron it out between them. Probably college was the answer, one with a good art department. He'd look into it and surprise her. Hands on the arms of his chair, he held the cigar with his teeth and uncurled his lips from it in order to say his last word.

"I have some things to do," he said gruffly. "I won't hear of this nonsense. Take a little trip and get it out of your system. Good night all."

He got to his feet, removed the cigar from his mouth to examine the ash, and walked into his library.

Sara's eyes lingered on his back with a touch of hunger. She was saying good-bye to him, and for a moment the recollection of his many generosities rose to soften her. She knew that they had been his way of buying off disturbance, but he had been kind too and after his fashion had tried to guide her with discipline. As she felt the idea of his kindness forming in her mind, she realized that it was the way she would describe an acquaintance who had done his social duty by her. Her eyes became ironic again and she said nothing. She arose to go to her room. There wasn't much use talking.

Mrs. Sander fluttered to her feet and came to Sara's side, putting one arm around her shoulders and peering with a flowery smile into her face. She fell into step beside her daughter and lowered her head.

"Darling," she said seriously, "I think my little girl has been getting ideas too old for her. As we get on in life – "

"Oh, for God's sake, Mother!" Sara burst out and bit her tongue. Mrs. Sander was hurt and withdrew her arm.

"I think she had better sleep over this," she said, nodding her head several times. "In the morning things – she will now, won't she?" She patted Sara's arm and kissed her on the forehead.

"Good night, Mother. Yes, we'll talk in the morning." She watched her mother go with her light skipping step, one arm held out as if to balance her. She was saying good-bye to her too, but there was no hunger in her, only a menacing determination to get it done with and be free. Her mother had never guided her but had left her to find her own way when she didn't know how. When she didn't resent this actively she regarded her mother as an unavoidable companion whose personality was antipathetic to her. She went to her room and packed.

She awoke early and had her breakfast before Mr. Sander appeared. Then she returned to her room, finishing her packing, and put on her hat and coat. Mrs. Sander responded promptly to her knock. She was still in bed, her breakfast tray across her knees, and she was arranging the small vase of flowers that always accompanied it. She seemed drawn and tired, and looked up at Sara questioningly.

"Well, darling," she said, at a loss for something to say, "where are you off to?"

"I've come to say good-bye, Mother," Sara said evenly, standing in the middle of the floor.

Mrs. Sander's mouth drooped and she patted the bed.

"Now, Sara," she said, "you didn't really mean all that. On such a lovely morning it just isn't – take off your things and sit down here."

Sara remained where she was.

"I'm sorry, Mother, but I'm going. I've rented a studio and I'm going to art school. I'll leave my address on your desk. This has been going on in me for a year. I've always saved most of my allowance and I'll manage until I can support myself."

Mrs. Sander measured her daughter and leaned back. When she spoke again, it was in a tone that Sara had never heard before.

"Why is it you dislike us so?" she asked.

Sara shifted her feet.

"That's funny," she said bitterly. "I think I ought to be asking that question."

Mrs. Sander's expression did not change.

"Yes, Sara," she said, "and you would have some reason to ask it. I've been thinking a great deal since last night. I should like to do better if you will let me."

Sara was touched. She could have listened to a flood of explanations unmoved. Her mother was looking at her steadily but there were tears on her cheeks. Sara closed her eyes for a moment.

"I'm afraid it's too late," she said. "You will have Jon."

"Yes, I shall have Jon," her mother repeated slowly, turning her eyes towards the window. "I'm sorry you can't say we shall have Jon."

"I don't see how I could," Sara remarked drily.

"I'll admit that, but I'm still sorry. I know now that we have been rivals for him." Mrs. Sander smiled ruefully. "I would rather have the part of him that you have won from me."

Sara blinked.

"He's been the only one that gave a damn," she said.

Mrs. Sander turned on her.

"You're wrong," she said with unexpected heat. "You can't go through birth and not give a damn. You'll find that out. I live in a very wonderful world." Mrs. Sander put her hand on her breast. "I gave you the right to find yours equally wonderful and asked no questions and put up no barriers. It's the best kind of giving a damn I could think of."

Sara grew contemptuous again.

"That isn't enough. Children want questions and barriers. Even Daddy did that now and then – when it occurred to him."

"I've tried to make amends about Jon," her mother said, stretching out her hand impulsively. "Can't we be quits?"

Sara took the hand without pressure and looked out of the window before answering.

"No," she said slowly. "It's not a matter of quits. I took what I could of Jon because there wasn't any other food, ever. I had to live. I can't live on quits now. I'm sorry."

Mrs. Sander removed her hand and let it fall on the coverlet.

"You're very cruel, Sara."

"I'm sorry, Mother," Sara repeated tonelessly.

"Very well," Mrs. Sander said in a whisper. "God be with you."

Sara glanced at her, and knotting her chin leaned down and kissed her mother's cheek. She had never seen that line in the older woman's face before. She noted carefully how it ran from the cheekbone to the corner of the mouth before she turned and walked out of the room.

Mr. Sander was very angry when he learned of Sara's departure. Such incomprehensible behavior simply did not happen. He had provided everything a girl could want and this was the thanks he got. Again he resented Sara's raising a problem. After venting his rage on one of his wife's particularly delicate flower pots by throwing it into the fireplace, he decided to wait a few days and see whether after all she hadn't gone off for a brief change of scene. Girls got upset easily at her age, he reflected, rubbing his chin. Better keep a cool head and wait a little.

The days went by without word from Sara and Mr. Sander began to boil again. A joke was a joke but this was going too far. He knew what to do. He'd show his strength and she'd come to heel soon enough. How could she live without his help? People brought up with certain niceties didn't live without them. He glowered at the address she had left. It was in a part of town he didn't know very well, and it would take a couple of hours out of his day to get there and back and knock some sense into her head. Inconvenient, but he'd better get it over with.

Sara opened the door to his knock. It was up three flights of stairs and he was out of breath. She did not seem surprised to see him and stood aside silently to let him enter. Meeting her there, not on neutral ground but in a place of her own choosing where she was mistress, even temporarily, made him a little uneasy. He recovered quickly, remembering his errand, and panting a little laid down his hat and gloves. Sara watched him for a minute.

"Well, Daddy," she said, "I suppose you've come after the lost sheep – so much more precious, for the moment, than the other ninety and nine."

Mr. Sander tried heavy wile and ignored her.

"Nice place you have here," he observed, looking about him with as much interest as he could muster. What he saw was an ample room arranged as a studio, bare except for a day-bed, two or three chairs, and modelling accessories. Opposite the entrance was an open door leading to a small bedroom with a bath beyond. Sara, having closed the hall door, came over and stood before him, her arms crossed and her intent eyes on his.

"Studio, bedroom, and bath, as you see," she replied. "But you didn't come to admire it, Daddy. Are you here as friend or enemy? Not that I don't know," she added maliciously.

"I'm here as your best friend," he said, "and your mother's. She is almost prostrated."

"Almost but not quite," Sara put in evenly. "After twenty years of ignoring her children, it must be a shock to find that one of them can ignore her, but it won't be fatal."

"You — " he began.

"Now don't call me names, Daddy. Mother was relieved to get rid of Helen and Dorothy by the honorable escape of matrimony. She'll be just as relieved to get rid of me by the equally honorable escape of a profession when she gets over her play-acting. She's sweet but futile, and you know it."

Mr. Sander stared at her in alarm.

"What about me?" he asked.

"Well, what about you? You're neither sweet nor futile. Now and then, when you thought of it, you gave me some training — as you did your horses. I can remember those times, little oases in the desert, but quite unconnected. I had to break trail from one to another myself, and you can't be surprised if I want to find my own oases from now on. You have a son and you don't need me."

Mr. Sander sat down abruptly on one of the chairs.

"You're a stranger to me," he said in a low voice, looking at her curiously, "and yet I've given you everything a father could."

"Everything except yourself," Sara observed. "Perhaps you haven't much of that to give, even to yourself. I've often wondered about it. Outwardly you've given me everything, and I'm grateful. By giving me everything you've made it possible for me to be indifferent to it. If I hadn't had so much, I'd have been curious about wealth and that would have diverted me. I can't afford to waste time."

"So now you're curious about poverty, is that it?"

"Not at all. That's a waste of time too. I've got to be an artist, and I don't care whether I'm rich or poor. I want to see life where most people live it, that's all."

"You'll see it all right," her father remarked grimly. "There'll be men, you know."

She laughed aloud and shook back her hair.

"I expect there will be," she said wickedly. "I've never seen lust face to face. I'm told it's important and quite prevalent. As you can imagine, my sex education has been neglected, save for a few hints from mother about the pollenization of flowers. I have had to get my own information."

Mr. Sander groaned but pulled himself together.

"I can go to law and make you come back," he said.

"But you won't," she retorted. "It isn't respectable, particularly as I'm quite capable of rolling up my sleeves and telling the judge that I don't want to live with you and mother, and why. The newspapers love to wash the dirty laundry of the rich."

Mr. Sander got to his feet and buttoned his coat. He couldn't avoid feeling a secret admiration for her. As a man, he could appreciate strength quite impersonally, wherever he found it, and in his world a good deal of selfishness passed for strength. He felt complacent over his defeat but played his hand out. In a dim way he could understand her.

"I shall of course stop your allowance," he said. "That may bring you to your senses when you're up against it. Where's your bank?"

Sara chuckled. "I wouldn't know what to do with a bank," she replied. "I've been saving my allowance for a long time and it's all hidden away in rolls of toilet paper. Give the allowance to Jon, or to the Home for Wayward Girls," she added mischievously.

He drew on his gloves carefully and picked up his hat.

"You're a damn fool, Sara," he said, almost diffidently. "Perhaps I am too. To go back to your very first question, I came as an enemy but I leave as your friend. I hope you'll believe it."

"That's because you go empty-handed," Sara answered, taking his arm. "I do believe it. If you should happen to think of me sometime, let me know how you're getting along."

He looked at her and smiled remotely.

Sara closed the door softly behind him. At last she was free.

She attacked her work with enthusiasm. She enrolled in the Art School and settled herself permanently in her new quarters. The days were very full, but she had expected that they would be until she had put things thoroughly in order. She never seemed to get to that point, however. Her great talent was recognized at once in the school and she was given the best teachers. They did what all teachers do in any art when they discover real talent; they loaded her with work and were more demanding of her than of their less gifted students. There was a great deal that she had to unlearn, for there had been a year or more, since her tutor left her, when she had shifted for herself and acquired some bad habits. Her new teachers pushed her to the limit.

She also had to learn how to live by herself and do for herself. For this she had no training whatever and no conception of how the smallest details of living could grow like monsters about her feet. They had an insatiable appetite for time. Finding no convenient place to eat near her apartment, she was forced to do her own cooking in the minute kitchen that opened out from the studio. The tiny cupboards were barely large enough to hold her few dishes and utensils, and she had to learn a great deal about cooking that she hadn't known before. The ice-box was so located that in order to open it she had to stand on the far side of it, against the sink, and then fall on her knees in order to reach what was inside. Once down, there was nothing on which to put the things she had taken out, and she had to arise unsteadily with the dishes balanced in either hand. The sink had an obstinate way of getting dirty. So had the bathroom floor and the window sills, where dust drifted in like smoke. Supplies had to be bought — food, soap, dusters, brooms and mops, pails, and a host of minor articles. Parts of things broke and had to be repaired. Fuses snapped and light bulbs burned out. Trash and garbage had to be prepared for removal. Laundry had to be fetched and carried. Floors must be swept and carpets beaten. Clothes needed mending. The windows had to be kept clean, particularly in the studio. She saw quite early that it would be a long time before she could support herself by her art and that she must live as cheaply as she could, in order to make her means last. If she were to fall ill everything would stop. The landlord's representative on the premises was singularly unimaginative. The school held sessions on Saturdays, and Sundays were filled with cleaning her quarters and repairing small obstinacies.

A weaker person than Sara would have given up. At times she felt a touch of panic when she thought of the future. She calculated that she could make her money last a year and a half, and if she got no paying art work by then she would have to get a job in order to live. The school had scholarships, but for tuition only. If she had to go to work she would either have to return home or else give up her art, let the studio go, and become a wage earner. She clenched her fists in the darkness of many sleepless nights and redoubled her efforts.

At Christmas vacation Jon visited her, bounding up the three flights in his eagerness to see her in her new life. She had begun to let details go, details of neatness in her rooms and in her dress, but she took pains for his visit and was tidy when he arrived. He took in every detail with breathless interest, and it warmed her to see that her hold on him had not relaxed. It won't, either, she said to herself, pushing back a damp lock from her forehead while she stood over the stove cooking their dinner. Jon threw himself down on the daybed and told her about his own life at boarding school. She followed it as women do, looking for overtones rather than for facts, and smiling to herself or at him when they fitted the narrative just as he had told it. It was the familiar dynastic path, but that gave her no concern; she had cut deeply beneath it and made her own a part of him that would not yield to anything so purely conventional. So long as he lived at home, her part of him was safe. If he married a rebel like herself they would be a threesome in arms. If he married another dynast she held the key to his nostalgia. Their parents had made no objection to his coming to see her, he said, but they were firm in making no move towards her themselves. It was a trial of strength; she had stunned them into believing that she could protect herself. Sara's mouth grew thin. She would be no prodigal daughter.

She allowed Jon to come only once during his Christmas vacation, once again at Easter, and once when his school recessed in the summer before the family went to New England for their vacation. She found it an increasing effort to prepare for him, but her instinct told her that rich young men grow tired quickly of the drabness and constriction of poverty. It was important to her to keep his interest. When he came she had no other company and made the dinner and herself as dainty as she could. He did not notice the growing shabbiness of her life or its steady drain on her. To him she was as she had always been, but in other surroundings, and if she seemed a little thinner it was only because they were both adrift in the quick flight of the adolescent years. If anything, his feeling for her had heightened; she was brave and daring and was living the romances he read about in school. If there were men in her life, he thought, they would be affairs of dark and passionate beauty. She was a goddess and her life a jewel being cut by firm strong hands.

Sara dreaded the summer. It stretched endlessly before her and promised a kind of heat that she had never known. School closed for two months, but she decided to review the year's instruction carefully and work by herself. She scheduled half a day and the evening for this and tried to get a part-time job in order to help her financial position a little, but as she had no ability except her art she found that no one wanted her. She had to resign herself to her plan of study and to passing the time as well as she could.

It was a hot, wet June. The city lost its crispness and began to simmer. Buildings sweated as if their outer walls were made of fat, and the streets softened. Materials went limp and sagged, and under the dancing heat waves the whole city seemed to be sinking in a long melting shudder to its knees.

Sara found it difficult to work and complained to her friends. They told her not to try too hard; the summer was the time to look around for possible contacts that might be useful later. There were openings in architects' offices, established sculptors needed student helpers, there was commercial work to be had; one must look around and become known. She found that many of her fellow students spent their summers in this way, giving parties or going to places where friends of friends knew someone of importance and might produce him. She began following their example and found that she enjoyed it, after her monastic winter. She had not realized that she was starved for sociability, and the ease and freedom of her new acquaintances at the school gave her pleasure. Streets and parks and homes were common property in the summer, and she drifted in and out of them all, looking for something that might lead to a paying job after her schooling was over.

She even gave a party herself. She planned it carefully and tried to make it a little different from the others that she had attended. She bought beer and pretzels, and decorations from the five and ten cent store, but her greatest care was in the discreet arrangement of her own work. The man with whom one of her friends was momentarily intimate knew the young architect who lived in the next block and promised to bring him. It was worth a small investment and some pains, but clearing the shabbiness from her apartment was more of a task than she had realized. It clung like a growth of fungus, and even when the dirt was removed it seemed to have gnawed at her things and left them frayed. Her company would be used to that, however, and she made her real effort over the lighting, turning the lamps into corners in order to light up the specimens of her work and cast enormous shadows of them on the wall beyond. The two beds, her few chairs, and the floor were all that she could offer for comfort.

The party was successful enough, Sara thought while she cleaned up afterwards, but she wondered if it had been worth the effort. Only a seasoned hostess is prepared for casual acceptance of her hospitality, and Sara's guests had swept through her rooms on a wave of idle laughter and chatter, as if passing through a station on their way to a train. They knew her work at the school and her covert exhibition was not new to them. Only a few glances of recognition floated off into the careful corners. But she had arranged them not for her friends but for the lion of the evening, and he had roared adequately if not in the full guttural of admiration. He was introduced to her as Bartram Fennel and was a tall, restless young man in his late twenties. She remembered having seen him in the street once or twice, walking with stale Sabbath fortitude beside a woman and a child of about seven. She had not recognized him until the change in him struck her; in her studio he was alone and urgent, and her first impression of him was that he ate with his eyes what he would later eliminate with his lips. Watching him while he nibbled his pretzels and drank his beer, she felt that he did it with a light brush, as if he were smelling a flower, a pleasant but unnecessary function, and he seemed to listen with his pores, not turning his head towards the sound. It struck her that sight was his major sense and was so precocious that his other senses could be interchanged at will or disregarded altogether.

She thought that he started a little when he turned to look

at her work, but she couldn't be sure. There was an unsleeping hunger in him that kept his eyes fretfully in motion, as if half blinded by a light behind them, and when they met hers their glance rushed at her in a smoky torrent, enveloping her for an instant before flooding past her. He was nice to her in his fleet way and murmured an appreciation of her work, but what he said was only the castings from his eyes. She thought that they would tell her more if she had time to watch them, and she gladly encouraged him when he asked her if he might come again. He dropped in several times during the next two weeks and sat slanted across the end of the daybed, his knees half drawn up and his eyes poring restlessly over her work while he told her about what he was doing.

He rarely looked at her directly, but when he did, for all the heated smokiness of his glance, she felt as if she were swimming in a sea of drift ice. He talked incessantly, having to clean out continually after the voracity of his eyes.

He was a slave to function, he said. "Mine is at the bottom of the list of the free arts. In music all form is in the head and ears; in painting and sculpture it's in the hand and eye; in literature it's in the mind's eye; in architecture it's in the body. Bodies bore me, that's why I'm restless. They're an infernal nuisance: they have to be rested and washed and educated and clothed and brushed and polished; things must be put into them, things let out of them, things wound around them; they must be placed just so, pushed about at a certain speed, kept at an even temperature, stood upright or laid horizontal, protected from wind and rain and sun, and kept out of harm's way.

"All of these boring precautions are monumentalized in a

house. The whole damn thing is a statue honoring the needs of the body. It shouldn't be called a house at all but a machine for living. The places for the various functions should be combined so as to make functioning easier. One should sleep in the bathroom on a combination of bed and toilet. The dressing-room and dining-room should be the same. The living-room should be in the cellar, for people are always a little furtive and hidden when they enjoy themselves. All of these things should be in a part of the house that is boxed in without windows. Above there should be a private room with windows all around it, for weeping and thinking. One shouldn't show one's tears any more than one's other exudations, and thinking is so difficult and unpleasant that there should be a separate place for it with a fine view and all kinds of comfortable chairs capable of tilting one to any position one likes. All of the household machinery should be in one place. When this has been done with mass-produced and prefabricated materials as compactly and cheaply as possible, the outside of the house should be put on separately and as extensively as money permits. Then you could really make it beautiful, for it would be practically divorced from functional needs, which are now so badly arranged that they make a house look as if it were bursting through its skin."

At first Sara reacted to this sort of talk as she would to a mild and pleasant anaesthesia. After a few visits, however, she began to see that his declared slavery to function was a form of conversational seduction. His ideas, which had seemed to her like disconnected ice floes among which she paddled coolly, now melted together into one large purpose, and her sense of danger, which had been merely a single-minded person's dread of anything unregulated, melted with it. She realized after a little while that behind his torrid eyes there was personality but not character, and she became sardonic and a little bored by his self-satisfied timidity. She even yawned once or twice while he was talking; it startled him and left him momentarily without a track. She found that it was easy to divert him, as easy as turning a turtle on its back, and when she had done so she saw that he lay there uncertainly, as unable as the turtle to right himself. It amused her to flick him over when she felt the heat mounting in him, and she began to wonder a little contemptuously whether he was capable of seduction in fact. That he was actually weak and timid robbed her of any fear of it, and she felt in herself a growing antiphony between her mastery of him and her curiosity to see the full flower of lust. As the pleasure of diverting him paled, her curiosity grew, and she sat listening to him with little manufactured signs of interest. She saw the fire grow in him and flicker towards her, and the nearer it came the more coldly she observed the signs of it. She knew that she would not flee from it or even flinch; she was prepared to take careful note of the whole experience.

Fennel had made no mention of her work since the night of her party. When he does, she thought, the moment will have come. She was watching him one evening, her chin in her hand, when she saw him pause and run his eyes over a small head that she was working on. His mouth was open and he was breathing hard. "I like that," he muttered and jumped to his feet. Taking her almost roughly by the arm, he led her in front of the statue and criticized it swiftly. He did it in such a way, without praising it, that she felt with a stab of pleasure that he accepted it as a serious work of art and needed only to point out where it fell short. She saw that he knew and that what he said was just. His artistic opinion was important to her, and she believed from the ring in his voice that it was an honest one, despite his purpose. He stopped and stepped back a little.

"It's good, you know," he concluded. "I can get you some work when you need it."

Sara smiled to herself. That's intended to be the key to the citadel, she thought, and when she turned to him to thank him she found her face crushed against his coat and his arms around her. She stood for an instant unmoving, amused by the heavy impact of silence that had fallen like a weight upon them. His face was disconcertingly close and she started back instinctively into focus, in order to see him better. As she did so, her mouth was blocked by his, and she could see above his closed eyes the tilt of his forehead and the blood beating like a hammer in a little vein below the hairline. When he released her she screwed herself around to see him directly, putting a hand on each of his shoulders to steady him. She had to know this, in detail and from the beginning and to the end. Methodically she made certain that there was no answering lust in her, only the clear crystal of curiosity. Her eyes swept his face. The mouth was open loosely and his shallow breath stirred a strand of saliva in one corner. The area of his face around the nose and its mobile muscles had narrowed and contracted a little, making a secondary center of tension in him. The corners of his eyes were pulled towards it and downward. Looking for an instant into his eyes she felt the whole experience of violation and inwardly fled from it, moving her head to his shoulder. Through the skylight she saw a bright star. The impersonal noises of the street came to her faintly, and there was no other sound save the ticking of her clock. He smelled faintly of horsehair and his whole body was moving against her, like a snake coiling. Time seemed to run out through her feet, leaving an open waste within her, and she stood quietly, belonging neither to herself nor to him. She had no other feeling now than a flat expectancy in which she floated while she watched the star. He was saying that he wanted her, and she felt him take her clothes from her while she stood there. Then without quite knowing how, she let him take possession.

"Look at me," she whispered. "Look at me until it's over."

The experience was not a very satisfying one to Sara. It slaked her curiosity, however, and she set to work modelling Fennel's lustful face, but she had no desire to be his mistress or anyone's. When her buzzer sounded from the front door during the next few days, she looked cautiously out of the window to see who it was, and if it was he she did not answer. When he stopped coming she gave it no thought until she received a letter from him, telling her that he had gone on vacation with his family until Labor Day. She did not reply to it, partly from a desire not to embarrass him and partly from relief. Much as she needed the work that he had said he could get for her, she felt instinctively that its price was concubinage, and she didn't want it on that basis. It would be a diversion from her work, and she wasn't ready for two powerful currents in her life. If an offer of work could come along as casually as this, so could others. She shook back her hair with a little shrug of her shoulders and forgot Fennel in a fresh attack upon her studies.

She did not think of him for three or four weeks. Then little by little he returned to her mind, not as the man she had known but as the thin white snake of fear. As the days passed it grew from a small line of thought to an angry terror that clogged her mind and blocked her footsteps. She lay on her bed for hours or stormed up and down the studio, wondering what to do. School had opened but she might need what was left of her money for this new thing. It would take its own time, and what would she do while she waited? There was no job that she could get. She was leaning against the mantel, her hand pressed hard against her forehead, when the door opened and Fennel walked in. He was grinning.

"I found the front door open," he said, starting towards her eagerly, "and wanted to surprise you. It doesn't look as if I had."

She merely turned her head away from him and he stopped. She closed her eyes for an instant and then fixed them steadily on his face.

"I'm pregnant," she said.

She saw that he went pale and sagged a little. He stood looking stupidly at her. The clock ticked loudly. It was the second time that silence had fallen on them like a thunder-clap, and she smiled sardonically. He saw it and grasped at the straw.

"Are you glad?"

"Of course not," she replied shortly. "Why should I be?"

Still she had not moved from the mantel. He gave a low whistle and looked down the creases of his trousers at his feet.

"Well," she said, "what shall I do?"

"It's mine, is it?" he asked.

"Of course. I never had a man before or since," she observed coldly.

He swore under his breath and suddenly flared with anger.

"Why the hell didn't you tell me if you didn't know what to do?" he raged. "What do you think I am? You're not living alone here in a studio as if you were innocent. A man's entitled to a break, you know." He stopped and laughed harshly, pointing to her writing table. "All right, we'll do something about it. Sit down there and write what I tell you."

She looked at him in dismay, but an answering flood of anger steadied her.

"Write it yourself," she said.

He gave her a sharp look of displeasure and sat down. He arose shortly and held out a piece of paper to her.

"There," he said with a steely gaiety. "Go to see this man and he'll remove it. Do you have money?"

She nodded vacantly.

"Well," he said, looking at his watch, "time's up. Good luck. I'm awfully sorry." He smiled at her dismally and closed the door behind him.

She watched him go in silence. Then she slowly raised the paper to her eyes without moving her head and saw that it was printed in a hand very unlike the writing in his letter. "Dr. Hrajek Pildenski, 231 East Park Street," it read. With a little spit of rage she dropped it to the floor and ground it under her heel.

His visit fixed her course of action. She'd go through this on her own line and let the baby come if it would. If the worst came to the worst, she could make him support it or get someone to adopt it; the hospital would handle that. She could work at the school up to the end and pretend that she had been married. The terror that she had felt was replaced by a savage determination to do her work and let nothing interfere with it, and she almost resented Jon's bursting in for his last visit before returning to school. If she was a little abstracted he seemed not to notice, but chattered happily about his summer while she sat and looked at the candle flame, thinking that she would show when he came again at Christmas and wondering how to put him off. She felt incongruous, sitting in her best dress as if nothing had happened, and she wondered why she had bothered to put it on for him at all. Why not tell him the ugly truth and let him shift for himself? She dismissed the thought almost as soon as it came; he had been the one human being that she had helped to create and mould, the one person that she loved. In a few years he would understand; she'd save him now, for the hunger in herself. She kissed him brightly when he left, not knowing when she would see him again.

The ensuing months proved to be more than she had bargained for. Waves of morning sickness swept over her, leaving her dizzy and shaking. At school the griping rot of nausea made it almost impossible to work and she had to struggle to sit upright. When morning sickness passed heartburn set in, but the nausea never wholly left her, and she had to neglect everything but food and sleep and work. She hadn't the strength to cook for herself, except breakfast, but she found a small restaurant near the school where she could get her dinner. It was dirty and the food was poor. She grew thin and pale and there were blotches under her skin. In December the baby began to show and her friends made comments; she fled from them on the pretext that she had married and was feeling too badly for company. The one bit of relief she had was a letter from Jon, saying that he had been invited to spend Christmas with a friend in the Middle West and wouldn't be home at all during the holidays.

Oddly enough, her work improved. Her fierce resistance to the threat of disability from the baby made her more acute, and her teachers began to train her for specific work that they could get for their outstanding students. By late March they had promised her a job with Ivan Bardelman when the school year was over. It was the best prize the school had to offer and it was hers. She had won. The faculty had hesitated because of the baby, but her talent was so great that they decided to let Bardelman take the responsibility himself. With almost her last money she bought a maternity dress. Somehow she must get through until the summer and she couldn't fail in the interview. She appeared in the sculptor's studio, pale but intent.

Bardelman squinted at her through eyes half closed above a curl of cigarette smoke.

"I won't waste words," he said curtly. "I've seen your work and it's good. I need your talent but not your baby. You must give me all your time."

"I suppose you know my record at school this year," she returned. "If I can do that while I'm having the baby I can do better after it's come."

He nodded slowly, unconvinced.

"Babies need care, so I'm told," he remarked, his eyes fixed on her. "So do husbands."

Sara's gray eyes burned back into his. She liked his directness and gambled on it.

"I won't waste words either," she said shortly. "I have no husband and I don't want this baby. I plan to get rid of it. I'd rather you didn't tell the faculty."

Bardelman's eyes shot open.

"Why should I? Why didn't you get rid of it while you could?" he was surprised into asking.

Sara shrugged her shoulders and looked away.

"Well, that's none of my business," he said with a trace of testiness and got to his feet. "Be ready to come July first. I think we'll get along." There was a ghost of a twinkle in his eyes and he held out his hand casually. Sara gave it a hard shake and looked her thanks.

"I'll be here," she said, and went out.

She felt a grim elation while she lumbered home, but she had no idea of how to support herself until summer. She clenched her fists in her pockets and thought hard. Turning into her street she nearly ran into Fennel. The shock of seeing him and the momentum of her success carried her past pride. He looked at her with distaste and began to edge by her, but she laid a hand quickly on his arm.

"Wait a minute," she said. "The baby will be here in a week or two. I need help."

His eyes froze, and the hardness in them made her lose her temper.

"I can make you. You know that, don't you?"

"Oh, it's blackmail, is it?" he replied unpleasantly. "There's a remedy for that too."

He fished in his pocket.

"Here," he muttered, holding out a bill. "This is all I have with me."

In an access of fury she struck his hand down.

"Damn you and your ten dollars," she cried out.

Her sharp movement stung him past restraint.

"You little bitch," he spit out at her. "It's your lookout, not mine. To hell with you."

He stood for a moment glaring at her. For the third time silence crashed down on them. She laughed bitterly and said nothing. With a little hiss he brushed by her and walked rapidly away.

Sara reached her studio weak and unsteady. Hard and direct as she was, pure rage bled her and left her with the feeling that there was skimmed milk in her veins. When she arose next morning she still felt white, and while cooking her breakfast she stumbled and fell against the stove. She threw out her left arm to protect herself; her weight rested for a moment on it and it broke her fall. Pain rose like a flame in her and she sat back against the wall, rocking a little and holding her left hand. Slowly she looked down and saw the seared flesh of her forearm; it seemed to be bubbling slightly and the wound was raw and dirty. She sat there for some minutes, gathering herself, and finally pulled herself to her feet. The arm had to be attended to. She finished making coffee and drank it black and unsweetened, smacking her lips and drawing in her breath slowly with each mouthful while she calculated her returning strength. Then she put on her hat and coat and set out for the hospital, wondering if the fall would hasten the baby, but the thumps and pushes against her inward perimeter continued as before and there was no new pain or soreness.

"Dr. Councill will see you in a few minutes," the nurse at the desk said to her when she reached the clinic. She sat and waited in a throbbing vacuum. The doctor was not long in coming. He treated her deftly and gave her brief instructions. He was a large man with white hair and a long nose that had a bump on the end. Good face, Sara said to herself, modelling it with her eyes. He smiled at her, noted her name and address on a card, and with a kindly nod when she thanked him told her to return in a week.

For the next few days she lived on small sums borrowed from her friends. When Saturday came she felt miserable and told her teachers that she wouldn't be back until after the baby had come. She was sure that her time was near, and once in the hospital she would be taken care of and fed until she was well and could face the world again. She bought a few supplies, enough to live on for a few days. Nothing to do now but wait.

She tossed fitfully all night and did not fall into deep sleep until dawn. When she awakened it was nearly noon, and she spent some time making herself a good meal. It would be the only one for the day and she was ravenous after her ordeal of the day before. She was careful around the stove, and the bandage on her arm reminded her that the week was up and that she should go to the hospital to have it treated. She felt weak and heavy. The meal was over and she was sitting on the daybed thinking about going when the first birthpain struck her. It was short and savage, and before she could pull herself together and recognize what it was there was another. She got to her feet and moved around for a minute or two, when the sledgehammer struck again. Sara was thoroughly frightened. She had planned on packing her things when she first felt pain and getting to the hospital in plenty of time, but the pains were swelling in intensity and were so atrocious that she could not move with any sustained effort. She sank back on the daybed, gasping. A hand seemed to reach inside her and twist, wrenching a great scream from her. She needed help quickly and labored to her feet to reach the door. Unlocking it, she flung it open and cried for help, but there was no answer. The house was small and there was only one other apartment on her floor. It was a mild warm day in early April and everyone must be out. The janitor's bell brought no response. The nearest telephone was on the floor below; she could get there but she didn't think that she could get back upstairs again. She might go downstairs and take the streetcar to the hospital; it was nearly half an hour's ride, with two changes, and she hesitated. The pains were battering her now, and while she was calculating how to reach the street and ask help of the first person she met, the sac burst and she was flooded.

Feeling as if she were wading, she slammed the door behind her, and half shrieking under the bombardment of pain made her way slowly towards the bathroom. She was trapped. Nothing now but to face it alone. Ideas came to her in snatches, like pieces of blue sky on a cloudy day. This was a quick birth; perhaps her driving herself so hard on poor food and little sleep had done it. Many women went through this alone. It would be over soon. She opened the last reserve of strength she had and fought to control herself. What to do next and where to have it? Stuffing her handkerchief in her mouth and bending double, she dragged a pillow from the daybed and waddled to the bathroom. Bathtub. She put the pillow in it and tore off her clothes. Groaning and screaming into her handkerchief and pouring with sweat, she climbed into the tub, braced her feet against its bottom wall, and dug her clenched fists into her eyes.

Jon walked up the street whistling gaily. He had missed seeing his sister at Christmas, and just before leaving school for the Easter holiday he had received a short note from her telling him of her good luck with Bardelman but asking him not to come to see her because she was taking care of a sick friend. He came straight from the train, wanting to surprise her, despite her sick friend. She had come out on top at school and had won its most coveted prize. She was wonderful, and he wanted to tell her so as quickly as he could. He meant to brush aside all of her objections and take her out on a real party; he was seventeen now and his allowance had been increased handsomely. He found the front door open and climbed the stairs.

Outside her door he paused a minute, thinking how surprised she would be to see him. He knocked the rapid little tattoo that was his signal and waited breathlessly. There was no answer. He listened for her quick footsteps, fearful that she might be out. He was about to knock again when he heard a harsh but muffled groan; that must be the sick friend. With a grunt of annoyance he tried the handle and it gave. He saw no one, but the door to her bedroom and the bathroom door beyond were open. From that direction came another hoarse noise, like a screech under a blanket.

"Sara!" he called sharply. Then he heard a cry for help and a sudden scream. It was her voice. Rushing through her room he flung himself into the bathroom and saw her.

"Oh my God!" she moaned. She turned her head away and sobbed.

He hardly recognized the contorted face. Her hair was hanging limply over her eyes and she was wrenching at her swollen body. There was blood in the bottom of the tub.

Jon staggered. He felt as if his body had been shot away from beneath his head. He saw his own hand raise itself, white and trembling.

"What's that?" he cried horridly, and pointed.

Sara fought for coherent breath.

"Help, Jon. It's a baby," she gasped. "Help me get it out."

Jon lurched to the wash basin and was violently sick. He had to take his head in both hands while he panted and choked back the bitter aftertaste.

"Help, you fool. I can't stand it much longer." Sara's voice came half strangled from the tub.

Jon staggered over to her and got shudderingly to his knees. "My God, Sara," he kept repeating over and over while she turned and twisted and beat her fists against the sides of the tub.

"Do something. Please do something."

"What can I do?" he cried in a frenzy.

"I don't know," she rasped out. "Do anything. Pull. Take hold of it if you can and pull."

Terrified he looked closer and saw a head, half born. Trembling so that he could hardly control his hands, Jon put his fingers on each side of the head and squeezed to get a purchase. The tiny head was soft and gave beneath his fingers. He jerked back, put his head down on the edge of the tub, and cried.

Sara's voice came to him, strangely low and pleading.

"Help, Jon, it's awful."

The idea that she was in danger broke through to him. Until now it was only a hideous dream without sequence or consequence. Suddenly his horror funnelled down into a blind rage at the thing that threatened her. "I'll get it out, God damn it," he growled. Gritting his teeth he reached for the head again, gripped it firmly, and pulled. It gave a little. He tried again and it gave a little more. There was blood on his hands; he wiped them quickly on his coat and pulled once more. Slowly and viscously the head moved outwards until it was all in sight. Jon stopped. There seemed to be a white veil over his eyes and his pulse was a vibrating flood that racked his body.

"What'll I do now?" he muttered.

"Try to get hold of the body and pull again," Sara whispered.

He followed her directions and groped with his fingers. He had to babble under his breath to keep steady; swearing to himself, he felt for the little shoulders as well as he could. He was clumsy and he knew that he was prolonging her pain, but he had to save her whatever might happen to the horrible growth that he was dragging from her. All at once the body came easily. He slid it onto the bottom of the tub and fell on the floor in a half faint. He lay there for a moment fighting for consciousness. Through the fog he could hear Sara moving languidly in the tub and then there came a small hoarse cry. He struggled to his knees and looked in. Sara was lying back on the pillow, her face dead white. They looked at each other for an instant like people who had never seen each other before; there was nothing but bare action between them, without room for gratitude or judgment.

The echo of the baby's cry roused Sara instinctively. She pulled herself forward and reached for the tiny body. With a noise like an animal she held it close to her face with one hand, and holding the cord in the other she bit it through. She laid the baby down and held the stub of cord between her fingers. Blood was streaked across her face and on her arms and breast. She turned her head away from Jon and shook.

Now that the danger was over, his strength returned to him as cold rage. From head to foot he shook with an anger outside himself. Its object was the dirty, ugly horror that lay between his sister's legs. It was responsible for this; no one who had suffered as he had seen her suffer could be held accountable. Her agony had washed away any fault in her. This barely brushed through his mind before he felt an overpowering desire for revenge upon the helpless creature lying quietly in her blood, the more responsible because of its indifference. Had it been able to jump to its feet and apologize he might have spared it, but the returning rush of blood to his head swept away every other thought except revenge. He bared his teeth.

"Give me that," he cried hoarsely.

She turned to him with a look of fright. For a fleeting moment her instinct rose to protect the child, and she reached for it with a little possessive cry. Then she dropped her hand. Her face hardened and she remembered. Jon. This must be the end of her with him. He was the only person that really mattered to her. The baby, her pain, the long dreadful months, Fennel. They flashed through her mind while she looked down at the bloody little lump that Jon was reaching for. Jon. He had seen her at this awful business and he would never look at her again. Her anguish struck bottom and rebounded as despairing hatred of what she had brought forth in such humiliation before his eyes. The hatred rose to join his anger. She shoved the baby from her with a gesture of loathing.

"Kill it," she breathed through set teeth.

Jon did not need to reply. He swept the small body to the end of the tub and with a vicious wrench turned the tap full on its face. Sara looked wildly about her. In her desperation she had to take part in this with him. She caught sight of the glass shelf above her on which were her toilet things. Raising herself partly with one hand, she groped on it until her fingers closed upon her nailfile. She lowered herself again with a grimace, and setting her mouth into a thin line she drove the nailfile again and again into the baby's softly heaving chest until it lay still.

Sara sat hunched over the body. There was no sound except the splashing of water. Jon turned off the tap with a shaking hand and sat down limply. Neither moved and the silence grew upon them.

"It's dead," she said at last.

He nodded his head idiotically, over and over.

"Yes, it's dead," he said, his voice abrupt, "and I don't give a damn."

They were both slack, now that the tide of anger had run out of them. After a few moments Sara raised her head wearily and looked at him. He returned her gaze, and her heart lifted to see that there was no condemnation in him. They saw each other again as they had been, but with a new burden that they both shared. They had killed the child for each other, and if anything they were closer than they had ever been.

She looked back at the baby and shuddered.

"Jon," she said, "we've killed it. You'll find some paper in the closet. Wrap it up, will you?"

He took a sheaf of paper at random from the closet and spread it on the floor beside the tub. Then he lifted the body onto it and hastily rolled it up. He was feeling ill again from reaction and the sweetish smell of blood.

"Guess I'll lie down a little while," he muttered.

She nodded. "Hand me my wrapper, Jon. I'll clean up while you rest. Then come in and help me out of here."

She looked better when he returned a quarter of an hour later. She was clean and her hair was tidied a little. The wrapper was around her as modestly as she could manage and she held up her arms to him.

"Now help me out," she said.

He put one arm around her shoulders and the other under

her knees, and lifted her out of the tub. She was pitifully light, he thought, setting her down gingerly on her feet. She clung to him and put her head on his shoulder for a minute.

"What time is it?" she asked.

"About three," he answered. "How long was this going on before I got here?"

"Oh, an hour or two; I don't know," she replied. "It can't have been long. I think I'd better lie down a while."

He picked her up again and carried her to her bed.

He lay down beside her and they stayed there quietly for an hour or more. Jon was numb; thought and action had withdrawn from him and left him in a leaden case of weakness. Sara fought for strength, trying to deepen her breathing and force the blood consciously through her flaccid muscles. She knew that she had to take the lead, and she had to think. Caught as she was, she struggled slowly back to action and forced herself at length to sit up. The room seemed steady around her and she moved her arms and legs carefully. She nudged her brother.

"Jon," she said, "help me up. I must try to walk."

He opened his eyes and for a moment could not understand. Then he shook himself and got to his feet. Taking his hands, she pulled herself erect and leaned against him.

"Now," she said.

She took a few steps, then pushed his arm away and took a few more alone.

"I can make it," she said more to herself than to him, and lowered herself slowly onto the bed again. She shook back her hair and took his hand.

"Jon," she went on, "we must think. We can't leave that –

that thing here very long. I have a plan. I was told to go back to the hospital today to have my arm dressed. I burned it a week ago. I'm going there now. If I take it slowly I can do it. That will make it look all right. As soon as it gets dark enough, you go out and dispose of the baby. Put it in an ashcan or leave it in an empty lot. You have your suitcase, and another package will look natural. Then go right home as if nothing had happened. But come back soon, will you? There are some things I have to tell you."

Her eyes searched his face hungrily.

"All right, Sis," he replied, "but I don't need to know. It couldn't be as bad as what we've gone through."

She patted his arm gratefully and got up.

"I have to dress now," she said and moved stiffly towards the bureau. He went into the studio and sat down on the day-bed, cracking his knuckles and thinking of what he had to do. It seemed like a good plan.

When she emerged from her room he helped her down the stairs. Just inside the front door she turned to him and flung her arms around his neck.

"God bless you, Jon," she said, crying.

He held her to him fiercely for a minute before letting her go and watched her while she walked painfully through the doorway and towards the streetcar.

He returned to the studio and waited impatiently. He was tense and nervous now and paced up and down, keeping a fearful eye on the paper package, as if it might cry out and denounce him or take to its legs and walk away. He was shivering, and the silence pounded in his ears. He went to the window a hundred times to see if it was dark enough, and when he thought that the twilight had deepened sufficiently he gritted his teeth, took up his suitcase and the package, and clattered down the stairs.

For a moment he had no idea of which way to go. Finally he set off to his left and walked swiftly away, looking about him furtively for possible repositories. Rounding a corner he had the misfortune to run into the arms of a policeman, and he caught his breath when he recognized the uniform. He muttered an apology, but the policeman stopped him.

"Wait a minute, young fella," he said. "Why in such a hurry?" He looked Jon up and down and suddenly frowned. They were standing beneath an arclight, and the policeman's keen eyes were running over him.

"Well, now, what's this?" There was a sharp tone in his voice and he pointed to Jon's coat. "This doesn't look so good, sonny." In a panic Jon looked down. The dried stains of blood where he had wiped his hands were barely visible on his coat. His heart beat in his throat. The policeman was bending over for a closer look at the package. Jon followed his gaze and to his horror saw that a small red spot had appeared at the lower corner. He made a quick move as if to break away, but the officer's firm grip closed on his arm.

"You'll come with me," he said brusquely.

When they reached the station house and the package was examined, it was found that one of the papers that Jon had gathered up was a laundry wrapping of Sara's, with her name and address neatly written on it.

Sara reached the hospital safely and sank into a seat. She was in pain and unutterably weary. She had to wait, and she huddled into a corner, hoping that another doctor would treat her this time. But it was the same one with the good face that she had seen before, and he entered the dispensary with another man. The doctor looked at her and moved towards the filing cabinet.

"What's your name, please?" he asked, and then added before she had time to reply: "By the way, you don't mind if my friend Judge Ulen looks on, do you? He's interested."

A flash of fear shot through her and she glanced quickly at the other man. Judge. So soon? she thought. No, it couldn't be, but she'd better take no chances. Most likely the doctor wouldn't recognize her; he must have lots of cases. The panic need of flight seized her and she had no time in which to think. The doctor was leaning against the cabinet, waiting.

"My name's Martha Tetlow," she said in a low voice.

The doctor rummaged in the file and then faced her reflectively.

"Let me have a look at that," he said, coming over to her. He undid the bandage. Sara felt the suspicion in him and shrank against the wall.

"Didn't I see this arm about a week ago?" he asked.

"I haven't been here before," she replied. "I bandaged this myself but it's been hurting me. I burned it on a stove."

She could feel the judge looking at her narrowly, but she had said it simply, as the flat truth. All she need do was to stand by it and say nothing more. The doctor was non committal and fortunately did not press the point. He ministered to her without further comment. She murmured: "Thank you," without raising her eyes, and left.

When she reached her house Jon and the police were waiting for her in the hallway. At the sight of them she gave a cry and fainted.

Jon had said nothing on being arrested, but the police didn't need his statement. When they discovered Sara's address they took him there with them on the chance that he and Sara would identify each other, and an inspection of the bathroom told them all that they needed to know. It was an easy case and they were kind to their young prisoners. They lifted Sara into the patrol wagon and drove her carefully. One of the detectives knew enough to notice that no afterbirth had been discovered, and he took her to the matron at the station house at once for an examination. She was then rushed to the prison hospital. She hadn't known about the afterbirth, and since it had delayed in making its appearance, she had made the trip to the hospital and back before it came. The prison doctor shook his head when he heard the details. "My God," he said under his breath, "we live and learn."

Sara and Jon were held without bail for Court and were duly indicted for murder. She had a narrow escape from septicemia and was kept in the prison hospital for a month. Since they were children of prominent people, the newspapers blazed with the story, and Mr. and Mrs. Sander came forward to do what they could. Mrs. Sander was unable to believe that the situation really existed, but her husband took hold with unexpected vigor. He had warned Sara about men, but he should have done more, and he felt unhappy about it. Since the man who had caused his daughter's downfall was unknown, he made it his personal business to find him, and through his influential connections he managed to keep the newspaper story going and to conduct a vigorous if aimless investigation. Sara wouldn't talk. At first he was angry, as men are who elect themselves to defend the reluctant honor of their women.

"No, Daddy," she said, shaking her head widely on the pillow, "you're sweet to bother but I won't tell you who he is. It was like stumbling over a chair in the dark. There's no use wreaking vengeance on the chair. I'd have to appear against him, and after what I've been through and what's ahead of me, it would be a waste of time. I have to stand trial for murder, you know."

He could see that she was frightened, however firm she was. He had learned from Jon about her winning the job with Bardelman, and despite the scandal and trouble that she was causing him, his secret admiration for her had increased rather than diminished. He knew power when he saw it and could appreciate it. Having failed her, he felt a new love for her.

"I thought I was neither sweet nor futile," he observed. She rolled her head on the pillow as if she hadn't heard him.

"As for your trial," he went on, "you have the best lawyer there is and he'll get you off."

Mr. Sander had become a little wiser and he read the look that she fastened on him.

"It would be the same," he went on without moving, "if Jon weren't in the case."

She laughed freely.

"That counts," she said and patted him. "I believe you."

Fennel, however, had no way of knowing Sara's attitude.

The papers told him that she had been seriously ill in prison, and for all he knew she couldn't talk, but he had reasonable ground for believing that she would name him when she could. He also read about Mr. Sander's determined search and he feared that he might be ferreted out through mutual friends who had seen him at Sara's party. It would not look well if that happened, but after all, people paid small attention to the morals of bohemians. His own friends would consider him the more interesting. He could draw the sting by coming forward voluntarily and then drop out of sight against the greater background of the murder. He calculated his chances carefully and one day, after having discreetly consulted a lawyer, he walked into the District Attorney's office with considerable dignity and gave himself up. He was promptly indicted for adultery, released on bail, and, as he had expected, forgotten.

Mrs. Sander fluttered into the hospital to see Sara as soon as she was allowed.

"You've seen Jon, I suppose." Sara spoke first.

"Of course," her mother replied. "The poor dear boy. What a dreadful thing – at the very outset too – " She stopped, shaking her head uncomprehendingly.

Sara smiled grimly.

"Yes, it was a tough break for him to happen in at the wrong moment," she observed.

Mrs. Sander looked puzzled.

"I didn't mean – " she said. "Oh Sara, how could you? Was it a very great love?"

"No, it wasn't," Sara said coldly.

"But I don't understand, dear."

"I'm sure you don't," Sara remarked succinctly. She felt a sardonic pleasure in telling her mother the bare facts. "I'll explain it to you clearly. I suddenly found his arms around me. I'd never seen that expression on a man's face before and I wanted to have a good look at it. When I'd seen it from start to finish I had what I wanted and forgot him. But I had the bad luck to get pregnant. See? And aside from these interesting speculations, there's the little matter of my having to stand trial for murder. Have you heard?"

She was almost beside herself and had trouble keeping a decent control. Mrs. Sander moved back as if struck.

"Sara!" she exclaimed under her breath.

There was silence. Sara's eyes flickered over her mother like sheet lightning. Mrs. Sander was twisting her fingers.

"Oh Sara, how could you?" she repeated. "A little baby — "

Sara laughed bitterly and opened her mouth as if to reply, but shut it again and shook her head in despair.

"I think I can understand," her mother went on, moving her chin slowly to one side in thought, "having an unwanted baby. But with Jon there – people do adopt babies. And spare him. Wouldn't that have been better?" She put her hand impulsively on her daughter's arm.

Sara wriggled up in bed to get a better purchase.

"Much better," she said mockingly. "Oh, ever so much better. But it so happens that Jon and I both wanted to kill that baby and for the same reason. We hated it. For what it had done to both of us. He did everything he could to save me. I was past caring for having to make him do it, so long as I got through. Then I did care. We both turned on the ugly little brat and killed it. You don't understand that, do you?"

"No," Mrs. Sander said sadly. "I think life is more precious than that."

"So do I," Sara commented, "when there's time to think about it."

"Even beyond thought," Mrs. Sander said, half to herself. "What use is a gentle upbringing?"

Sara lost control.

"I'll tell you," she retorted venomously. "I didn't know until I got into this bed that there was such a thing as afterbirth. Your precious little hints about bees and birds and pollen didn't include anything so nasty. I got up and went to the hospital and back with the afterbirth still in me. If you had told me the truth instead of fairy tales, your darling Jon and I – "

"My darling Jon?" her mother interrupted. Sara met the challenge.

"My darling Jon, then, and I might not have been in this fix. We'd have waited for the afterbirth. We might have thought it out better and avoided detection."

"Is that the only – " Mrs. Sander put in. "To avoid detection?"

"Well, what?" Sara almost shouted. "Oh, let's not talk. We'll never get anywhere."

"I've tried to do the best I could. I've had my hard moments too, Sara. I wish you'd believe – "

"I told you once your best wasn't good enough, Mother. Intentions are fine up to the point where the chips really go down. As for Jon," she added cruelly, "he's closer to me than ever. Personal relations thrive on hard experiences better than on moonbeams. Oh, Mother, do stop! Let it go as it is."

She paused and the silence fell like rain. Sara said nothing more. After a few minutes Mrs. Sander got to her feet with a helpless cry and went away.

Jon and Sara were of course separated in prison and saw each other only when their lawyer interviewed them. He was Homer Martin, the leading criminal lawyer in the State. To him the case was simple, but the Sanders and their friends pestered him needlessly about it. He set them all to work compiling an impressive list of character witnesses. "I don't want Judges and Governors and presidents of banks," he told them. "I'll allow you half a dozen of that variety and no more. Their minister is all right. What I really want is plain people who will make the jury think that the kids are rich but human. Give me the milkman and some Boy Scouts and a truck driver, if you can find one. It won't be easy with youngsters from their walk of life, but their case depends on it. Get busy now and don't bother me."

With Sara and Jon he hit just the right note and gave them confidence. He talked to them like the engineer who was driving their train.

"Now look here," he said to them. "The case against you is clear. You know what they've got on you and so do I, but that doesn't mean you'll lose. It may. I never guarantee an acquittal to any client, but that's what I'm going to try for.

"I feel confident in saying that there is no danger of a first-degree verdict. The necessary elements are there, but since the only penalty for first-degree murder is death, it is my experience that no jury would impose it in a case like this upon defendants like you. It is theoretically possible but altogether unlikely. Nor is there any chance for manslaughter; that needs rage and provocation, and you had no legal provocation. It's second-degree murder or nothing. The punishment for second-degree is, in general, anything up to life imprisonment. It depends on the judge. It will be Ulen: he's fair, he'll listen to anything, and he isn't prejudiced. I can't guarantee either that you won't have to do some time in jail. That will be bad for you, but after all this is a murder case. Needless to say, we'll fight it all the way to the Supreme Court if there's a verdict against you.

"My plan to win the case outright has no magic in it. We lawyers are not magicians. You must go to trial before twelve plain people, and what appeals to plain people is what counts. I won't fight the State's case much. There isn't anything to fight with, on the facts. Then I shall put on an array of character witnesses and you shall not take the stand. The right kind of character testimony is the best defense I know in a case like this. You couldn't tell the truth and get off. If you say nothing, the jury will be free to decide whether under all the circumstances the truth should be charged against you, but they wouldn't be free to do that if they heard you admit it.

"You sit there and be yourselves. I'll do my best for you."

Last case of the season, Ulen said to himself, walking out to open Court. It was the middle of July, and the damp, heavy weather hung in clots upon the city. He was tired and looked forward eagerly to his vacation, like a diver struggling up towards the fresh air. He stood while the clerk intoned the session of Court and then lowered himself into his chair, the thin silk of his robe floating into place around him.

The docket on the bench before him said: "State v. Sara Sander; State v. Jon Sander. Murder." The name seemed familiar somehow, and he leaned back to see the prisoners' faces when they came through the door behind the jury box that led from the cellroom. Terribly young, he thought, when they came into view. The boy was lean and tall, with a touch of the Irish poet about him. The girl was rather older, and her eyes were bent on Ulen when she entered the courtroom. He searched his memory. It was not a remarkable face, save for a steely singleness and the steady brushfire of those gray eyes. He remembered a rumpus in the newspapers, probably this case; the name was well known. A child killed, he recalled, rubbing his chin against his fingers. Messy. Such a case should be tried against a neutral background, so that all of the colors could stand out accurately, everything matter of fact and no funny business. He looked around to see which lawyers he'd have to work with; it made a difference. Dalling was sitting quietly at the State's table. All right. Dalling wasn't given to balloon ascensions into the clouds of righteous indignation. He worked hard but drily and made the State the impersonal or implacable or unobserving thing it ought to be on proper occasion.

As the prisoners came to the bar to be arraigned, Ulen saw Homer Martin arise and stand beside them. All right again. Martin was the best there was. He fought bitterly with his mind but never threw away a word. When he spoke, whether to a witness or to the jury or to the Court, his thought was so clear that it needed only the sparest words to carry it. A trial rolled on a vehicle of words, and they were important, particularly those of the court professionals. With these lawyers it would be a fair trial and the situation might judge itself. That was always best, and he leaned back with a breath of relief. The voice of the clerk was droning the indictments: " – feloniously, wilfully, deliberately and of his malice aforethought upon the body of an unnamed child, within the peace of God and the dignity of the State then being, did make an assault, and upon the said body did inflict harm and divers mortal wounds, whereof the said unnamed child after languishing did die: and hence the said Jon Sander, yeoman, the said unnamed child did kill and murder, contrary to the peace of God and the dignity of the State aforesaid."

The young prisoners listened to the medieval language as they might watch the flow of water across the arches of an ancient viaduct. When it ended they murmured: "Not guilty," in turn, and watched the clerk to see if there were more.

"And so saying, how will you be tried?"

Martin whispered to each of them before the question was finished.

"By God and my country," they repeated.

"May God send you a safe deliverance," the clerk concluded. "Take seats, please."

Martin worked hard over the jury. It was one of the three points in the trial on which he had decided to bear down; the others were his character witnesses and the last speech to the jury, to which he would be entitled by reason of not putting his clients or any eye-witness on the stand. He used all of his challenges trying to select a jury of quiet elderly men and of elderly women who had either a great many children or none. When it was over he leaned back with satisfaction and prepared himself to let the State put in its case as quickly as possible without lending it any emphasis of his own. He knew that he had no chance to break it down, and without eye witnesses the testimony of no one but doctors and police officers might make it seem professional and bare. The less emotion the better, and it would necessarily be short. Luckily there were no confessions to deal with.

He had to object, however, when Dalling tried to put in evidence a picture of the murdered child. Since no one could identify the body, the police had photographed it. Ulen gave the picture a troubled look and sustained Martin. The testimony of the coroner's physician and of the policeman who had found Jon was enough to prove the *corpus delicti,*[3] added to the doctor's examination of Sara and the discovery of the undelivered afterbirth. The still horror of the picture was out of place in the kind of atmosphere that he wanted in his trials.

Dalling proved without difficulty that the child was Sara's. Minutely careful, he produced medical evidence that the severed piece of cord fitted both mother and child. The coro-

[3] The body of the crime. In murder cases it's the corpse, in theft cases it's the thing taken, and they must be produced or accounted for beyond a reasonable doubt. Once upon a time a young man slept with another man in a crowded inn. He awoke early and went to his home. Later the other man was found to have disappeared, leaving a pool of blood in the bed and a trail of blood leading to the end of a pier, where it vanished. The young man was pursued, convicted, and hanged. He was so tall that his feet touched the ground slightly and his friends who crowded around him managed to support him a little. After he was cut down they were able to revive him and smuggled him out of the country. Some time later, in China, he met the man whom he was supposed to have murdered: the victim had been bled the day before, and the wound not having healed, he went in search of a doctor during the night but was set upon by an impressment gang and shanghaied aboard a ship. That sort of thing happened a few times before the law was changed to provide that the State must produce a corpse before trying to make one out of the prisoner.

ner's physician had of course held an autopsy, and he testified that the child had lived after birth. The circumstances of the murder were equally clear: the nailfile, the fatal wounds in the baby's chest, traces of water in the tub and in the baby's throat and lungs. The coroner's verdict had been death by stabbing or drowning or by both concurrently.

Ulen looked up in surprise when he heard Councill's name called. Then he remembered; that day in April when he was at the hospital, the day John Longa had broken his arm. Well. This was the mystery the rhinoceros had spoken of. He could see the girl's face and the light that had flashed on in her eyes when she heard Councill mention his name. Must have been scared he had come for her. She'd given some false name, Councill was testifying. Yes, he recalled thinking then that she was lying. Lying seemed less and less important to him, so long as it entangled no one else. He thought he'd lie himself if he were sitting in her place. Councill gave him a little twinkle from the off-jury side of his face when he left the stand, to which Ulen responded with a slight lift of one eyebrow.

It was Martin's turn to sit up in surprise when Dalling, consulting the bill of indictment for his next witness, called out: "Ivan Bardelman." Dalling noticed his opponent's slight start with a flicker of amusement. Bardelman was his star witness; the defense couldn't know what was coming. Martin turned to Sara, but she only shook her head in bewilderment and said nothing. She felt numb. She had thought that he would probably read about the case, but she couldn't imagine why he should be brought into it actively. He didn't want her baby, he had said to her; and now he had it, in a way.

He'd be angry with her and retract his offer even if she got out of this without a jail sentence.

Dalling asked the witness his name and occupation and confirmed his offer to give Sara a job in his studio.

"Did you interview Miss Sander?" he asked. Bardelman said that he had. In the way intelligent witnesses do, he answered the questions shortly and without explanations. His Slavic face was a mask but his small, keen eyes blinked incessantly. He seemed wary and disapproving of the situation in which he found himself. Dalling felt it, and as such witnesses are a rarity, he proceeded cautiously.

"When was it?"

"Shortly before the end of March. I forget the exact date."

"Did she come to your studio?"

"Of course." He gave a mirthless snort of impatience.

"Did you discuss her – er, condition?"

"I did not."

Dalling looked at him. Bardelman looked back; he was answering the questions exactly as put to him.

"Did you discuss the baby, then?"

"I did."

"What did you say about it?"

"I said I wanted her talent but not her baby."

Dalling dropped his voice ominously.

"And did she say anything about the baby?"

Bardelman looked accusingly at his feet.

"She did," he replied after a moment.

"What did she say?"

Bardelman cast an ironic glance at Ulen. Martin heard Sara catch her breath behind him, and arose.

"I object," he said.

It was one of those moments in a trial when neither judge nor defense counsel knows what is ahead and must rely on instinct. Most likely it would be a damaging statement.

"I will sustain the objection so far as the other defendant is concerned," Ulen said slowly, his eyes on the open docket before him. "No connection between this witness and him has been shown. As to Miss Sander, the objection is overruled, for obvious reasons." Martin subsided.

"Shall I answer?" Bardelman looked up again. Ulen nodded.

"She said that she didn't want the baby and planned to get rid of it."

It was Dalling's trump card, his best bit of evidence to support a first-degree verdict.

Surprised as he was, Martin was too old a campaigner to be taken unawares. He looked around casually, as if he had expected this evidence and had a perfect explanation for it. He had no ground for objecting to it. There was a moment of electric silence while the implication of the testimony sank in. Bardelman took advantage of it.

"She didn't mean murder, however," he said grimly. Dalling arose with authority.

"I move that the last remark of the witness be stricken out as unresponsive," he said coldly.

"Strike it," Ulen said.

Dalling was resuming his seat when Bardelman again gave tongue.

"Just the same, she didn't mean murder," he repeated obstinately.

Dalling shot to his feet.

"Your Honor," he said with sharp indignation, "I request that you caution the witness."

Ulen swung towards the witness stand.

"Mr. Bardelman," he said equably, "I'm sure you are intelligent enough to know that on the witness stand you are supposed to speak only when spoken to."

Bardelman looked up at him as he would at an antagonist across the dinner table.

"I was spoken to," he replied deliberately, "and I made the only intelligent answer a man could make. Any fool could see it by looking at her."

Ulen raised his eyes briefly to the jury box.

"There are twelve people – not fools, but people like you and me – " he observed, "who are looking at her now. They will look at her for a longer time than you did. Possibly they will reach the same conclusion you came to; possibly not. Aren't you being a little impatient of our methods?"

"I speak my mind," the other answered brusquely. "That's what she made an impression on. Isn't this a court of justice?"

"No, it isn't," Ulen replied tartly. "It's a court of law. I presume you are aware of the difference?"

"I must admit that it escapes me," Bardelman observed with a trace of sarcasm.

"Then I will explain," Ulen went on a little wearily. "I take it that you call your workshop a sculptor's studio, not a studio for beauty – or truth or reality or whatever it is you try to put into your work. Hammer and chisel and stone and plaster are your tools. Law is our tool. If you make a beautiful or truthful or realistic statue you have achieved your purpose. If we make our law do justice we have achieved ours." He leaned forward suddenly and spat out at Bardelman: "And we are no more willing than you are to suffer gladly the kibitzers who stand around and criticize our technique. I will ask you to answer questions as put to you and suspend your judgment until the end of the case."

Bardelman seemed unimpressed.

"What's justice?" he inquired acidly.

The courtroom was tense and the newspaper reporters wrote busily.

"Whatever the State and these prisoners take away with them from court," Ulen snapped. "It may be bad, as one of your statues might turn out to be bad. But not if we can help it.

"The incident is closed. Please proceed, gentlemen."

Bardelman gave him a surprised look and was silent. Sara gazed at his carelessly slouched figure with admiration. She could see that he hadn't the least concern for her but only for the integrity of his own impressions. The judge must have felt that too, or he wouldn't have risked the encounter. She had held her breath at Bardelman's temerity, for fear that Ulen would get angry and hold him for contempt of court. But he hadn't. Bardelman had won a point for himself and for her. The judge had won a point for his court. She felt a thrill of pleasure. This was life at its best; these men were working with absorption at a rough job without a trace of sentiment. A sense of confidence began to glow in her; it would come right for her, whatever the result might be. They were all playing their parts full and hard, as she had played hers, bad as it was. All the pressures seemed to match. A swift look at the jury assured her that they too had caught the spirit of the case and would do their best; they were leaning forward with full attention. That was all she needed from them. The power of her story and the power of this trial would mesh and spin her life into balance again. She sat back and closed her eyes, but she was still troubled. How could the power of her story be brought into the trial? The horror of the State's case should be matched against the horror that had driven her to the murder, but she was not going to take the stand. Without her they couldn't know. She had to trust Martin. She didn't know his business and he was the best lawyer in the State. She seemed to have lost her footing again.

She roused from her reverie in a welter of uncertainty to hear Dalling say: "Cross-examine."

Martin waved a genial hand.

"No questions," he responded with a smile.

Court adjourned for the day after that, and Sara spoke to Martin about her idea.

"Let me tell my story," she pleaded in conclusion. "All they know now is what they've heard against me. They ought to know what I felt and why I did it, shouldn't they? They mightn't let me off, but wouldn't it help with the judge?"

Martin looked at her with tired eyes and then at Jon. If she were alone, he might risk a plea of guilty and stake everything on a light sentence. But the lightest he could hope for would be the Women's Reformatory, where she would have to stay for at least two years. To admit the killing at all meant to plead guilty and lose the chance of an acquittal. He tried to explain it to her.

"And what about Jon?" he ended.

Sara colored, but recovered swiftly. She had forgotten him; not him exactly, for their positions were of the same cloth, but his separate rights in the outcome.

"I could clear him," she ventured.

Martin looked at her with reproach.

"Don't be a fool," he said acidly. "They have the fingerprints of both of you, and Dalling will put them in tomorrow.

"I have the responsibility for your defense and you must do what I tell you. There's a real chance for acquittal. Character testimony may of itself raise a reasonable doubt, and that's all you need. You're young, and the jury may decide to overlook what you've done. The baby lived only a few minutes. It may not be a very big chance but it's worth keeping open. Jon's entitled to it. After what Bardelman has done for us, the only possible verdicts are second-degree and acquittal, as I told you before. Why throw up one alternative?"

She nodded her head in acceptance and they were led away to their cellrooms.

Jon spent an unhappy and sleepless night. There had been many others like it during the long three months of awaiting trial, while he sweltered towards a maturity of view about the case. His eyes bored into the darkness around him and his mind picked at an opaque curtain of thought. The awful hour or two with Sara was not a piece of his life that he had shaped and twisted into an unrecognizable grimace of time. It was rather a separate and malignant outer force, which had so shaken him and ripped him loose from every familiar mooring that it was only faintly, from the outermost perimeter of consciousness, that he had been aware of what he was doing. Ordinarily there was no distance between thought and action. Suddenly they had been stretched apart by one fierce tension, and from the perimeter his mind had looked back through the vibrating distance to the center where, dimly and alone, his instinct had done what it had to do. The tension had been unbearable. It had even drained his sight of color until the blood had stood out black against the whitened body of his sister. He had lived the time in a tight but empty space, and when his hands had moved within his range of vision they had been like separate things on missions of their own.

Jon tried to get clear in his young head the source of the stark force that had fallen on him and made him do without thought what it demanded of him. He had been taught to believe that he was a free agent, but he had not been free in the grip of this. All that he had provided was the bare energy, and he hardly knew how he had done that. Now that it was over, he had difficulty in finding his way backward through it as one does through the fading recollection of a dream. He knew what he had done but not why. Groping through the curtain, the only thread that he could find was his love for Sara, but why it should have made him act as he had did not come to him clearly until the last night of the trial. He followed the thread back of the experience in her apartment, and gradually he saw it widen into a broad trail that led as far as he could remember into the earliest years of his life. Everything along that trail fell into place and became a strand in the relationship that he had built up with her. He tried to think of all the contacts they had had, resting for a moment on each, and while he did so there came to him at last the knowledge that he had acted at the moment of crisis in the way his life until that moment had prepared him to act. The momentum of the idea carried him past the particular personal objective into the penumbra of thought where the great impersonal ideas are born. Not only that moment, he thought, but every one; I act at every instant in the way my life until then has prepared me to act.

He stretched himself with a sigh and the tension and fear of the past months slowly left him. He rested for a long time in a dead pool of thought, and his mind ceased looking backward and rested before turning to face ahead. He had now a clear nexus with what lay behind him; there remained the path before him to be cleared and charted. Beyond the new curtain of the future he sensed the bulk of a necessary decision. He raised himself on one elbow and watched the darkness dilute with dawn from the high barred window of his cell. His relationship with Sara had not been ended, it had only been proved. There was more to be done and it was his to do. He had taken the initiative in killing the baby; his instinct had seen as if out of the corner of its eye that she had followed him and not led. A deeper instinct told him that he would always take the final great actions between them. Strong as she was, she seemed to use up her strength short of the ultimate point, and beyond that point she was uncertain. He saw too that he had killed the baby in a rage born of his love for her, but that she had joined him in the act for purposes of her own. He knew that she loved him, but behind this there was another drive in her so powerful that she could not carry through any other force at variance with it; it drove her to correct one mistake by another. He remembered her quick start towards the baby when he had reached for it, and then her small white arm flailing it. He shook his head sadly at the realization that he had seen her as she was, and because he loved her he felt for the first time, like a sharp taste in his mouth, the awful loneliness in her.

He got up and walked up and down his cell, thinking hard. Recalling her words and Martin's when court recessed, and weighing every aspect of the trial as clearly as he could, he came to the conclusion that an acquittal was impossible. How could they? Martin was a good lawyer but he was only a hired technician. Sara had accepted him. Jon couldn't. Without their story in the case there was an incompleteness that rested badly. Dimly he felt that unless the whole thing were known, the case would sag into distortion at the end and the result be wrong. That was the way they played their games at school, even the bad ones, keeping at least the integrity of sustained effort; then there was nothing to regret. There were prizes given for effort, regardless of the score. This was no game that he was playing, but it was the judge that gave the prize when he passed sentence. Martin wasn't like his teachers; they were more than technicians, they lived with the boys in a way no lawyer did. Jon felt that he had nothing better to go by. Their way seemed fuller and deeper than Martin's, a better preparation for this moment. Even for Sara, whom he would be taking with him.

He lay down on the cot again and thought out every detail that he could foresee. It was a heavy burden for his slender shoulders to carry. When they came to take him to court he was pale and drenched with fatigue, but he had made his decision.

After Court had opened, Dalling put on the fingerprint expert, who testified that the prints on the faucet of the bathtub were Jon's, and those on the nailfile were Sara's. Then he arose.

"The State rests," he said.

Martin made no opening speech to the jury but waved to his character witnesses to come forward. They had been chosen skilfully. They were tradespeople and neighboring farmers and Scouts. The gentle creatures with the intriguing dark skin, who had fascinated Sara when she was a child and had remained her friends, appeared for her. After great effort a truck driver had been found; he knew only a few people who knew the defendants, he said, scratching his head, but his appearance was impressive. Sandwiched in casually were a few people of prominence. Old Judge Parkinson, whose finances were discreetly guarded by Mr. Sander's investment house, felt that it was the least he could do. The Sanders' minister testified with the clean but indefinable fragility of his calling. One or two well-known businessmen followed. It was an excellent showing; only a few questions were asked of each, and the rapid cross-section of occupations and personalities was interesting. The jury paid close attention.

When the last one left the stand Martin sighed. It had gone well. Now for his speech, his major point of effort. He'd have time to salt it down into shape while Dalling spoke. He arose slowly and faced the bench.

"The defense rests, Your Honor," he announced.

He was settling himself into his chair when Jon arose quickly from behind him and strode towards the witness stand.

"I want to testify, Judge," he said in a clear voice. He was beyond Martin's reach, but the lawyer would not have dared to restrain him openly had he been able. Martin controlled himself quickly and gave no sign of surprise. Sara glanced up at Jon with a start. The courtroom, which had relaxed as if for a change of scene, tautened again. Ulen raised his eyebrows sharply but said nothing.

Jon ignored Martin and began to speak as soon as the oath had been administered. He told the story briefly but in detail. When he reached the murder he said: "I turned the water on its face but I was afraid it wouldn't be enough. I looked around and saw Sara's nailfile on a shelf above the bathtub and took it and stabbed the baby. Then I washed off the nailfile and dried it on a towel and gave it to her."

"Why didn't you put it back on the shelf?" Martin asked. He had to forestall Dalling and take the chance that Jon had thought of it.

"I don't know," Jon said slowly. "When it was over I felt sick. It was hers and I just gave it to her."

Martin waited a minute to see if he had finished and then said: "Cross-examine."

He had been thinking swiftly and turned to Sara.

"Sit still," he growled at her. "He may have helped us at that, the damn little fool. You can't get up and give him the lie, and you can't say you turned on the tap but wiped it before he turned it off. Don't make a circus of it."

She nodded slightly and leaned back in time to see Dalling shake his head with a grim smile and say: "No questions."

Every eye in the room was on Jon when he left the stand. That he had lied to help his sister was as plain as if the untruthful words had come from his mouth in air of a different color. But it was a wholesome lie and no one thought the worse of him for it. The sense of pursuit that is in every trial was satisfied. Guilt had been acknowledged and the chase was over; the lie was extra and it was admirable. He hadn't done it out of gallantry, however, and he sat down oblivious of the unexpected credit he was getting. To testify was the only way to get their side of the story into the case, and to lie about her part in the killing was the only way that he could think of to leave Sara free and not force her to take the stand herself. He knew the story was thin, but he thought it was enough to cover her.

While he had been speaking Sara was tempted to follow him to the stand, but when he had finished there was only an instant in which to act, and she was divided. She couldn't let him take the full burden, but the story was in and she trusted Martin. Her life, standing behind her moment of decision, led her instinctively along the major path that it had made for her, which had always been herself. Its secondary urge, her love for Jon, rose weakly and too late. She made a slight movement to arise, but the instant passed and she saw that Dalling was already on his feet. "Members of the jury – " he was saying to them, beginning his speech. She'd make a circus of it if she got up now.

Sara slumped in her chair, and covering her face with one hand wept quietly.

The jury was out for only half an hour. Its verdict was, as against both defendants, guilty of murder in the second degree, with a recommendation of mercy.

Martin had talked with his clients and with Mr. and Mrs. Sander while the jury was out. Best to leave it as it was now, was his advice. After the verdict had been recorded he led Jon and Sara to the bar.

"I have no motion to make, Your Honor," he said briefly.

Dalling arose and moved for sentence.

Sara leaned forward and addressed Ulen. "Judge," she said, "Jon was wrong. I used the nailfile on the baby. The rest of what he said was true." Jon looked at her but could say nothing.

"Yes, I know," Ulen answered. "That was very clear. But there is something else that isn't at all clear. My experience is that the more horrible a case is, the more reason there must be to look behind it for a very simple cause. I don't believe that the ordinary man or woman revels in horror for the fun of it. How did you come to have this baby?"

Sara's eyes did not shift from his face. She was back on her own track again.

"I'm a sculptor," she said. "I'd never seen that look on a man's face before. When he put his arms around me, there it was, and I saw no other way of getting it complete. I got it but I also got a baby."

Ulen's eyes did not leave hers.

"Mr. Bardelman," he called, "will you come up here, please?"

Bardelman detached himself from the spectators and came forwards.

"Did you hear what Miss Sander just said?" Ulen asked him. Bardelman nodded. "Does it make sense to you?"

The sculptor snorted. "Of course it does," he replied. "That's what genius can do to a person."

Sara looked up at him quickly at the word.

"Is your offer to her still open?" Ulen inquired.

"It is. If you think that a thing like this would prevent my taking such a talent you're very much mistaken."

"Oh?" said Ulen, leaning back. "I hope you realize that I have to keep one eye on the wall of laws around society and the other on the rights of those who make holes in it."

"I'm interested in talent," Bardelman said shortly. "She'll give back to society more than she's taken if I can get my hands on her. Sending her to jail would be nonsense."

"Mr. and Mrs. Sander, please come forward," Ulen said, ignoring him. "How did your daughter happen to be living where she was?"

Mr. Sander looked bleakly at the clerk's desk below the bench but found no reply. His wife leaned forward.

"She went away, Judge," she said.

"And you let her go, I presume?" he went on.

"But we did everything – " she continued. "And dear Jon – he's not, you know, really."

"I begin to get the idea," Ulen said slowly. "You did everything but make it possible to keep her. When the pinch came you found you couldn't. You've never known your children, and that's tragic. That's all, thank you."

He turned back to Jon and Sara. "I can't sentence you now. In my position it is not wise to decide on a sentence until everything is before me. Life is precious, under our laws, and you have taken it; but your life is precious too, and I must balance those ideas and see what is best to do, not only for you but for all children, who are less secure in their right to live because of what you have done. Today is Friday. I will remand you to prison until Monday, and will be ready to sentence you then.

"I notice from my docket that one Bartram Fennel has been indicted for adultery in connection with this case and has pleaded guilty. The disposition of his plea has been deferred pending the outcome of this trial. I direct that he appear here on Monday also."

Saturday he lay fallow and did nothing but read and walk in the woods. He knew what he wanted to do but he had to test it. On Sunday he went with his wife to meeting. Sam and Ida Willen, with whom they were to have lunch, were there too. The Willens were not Quakers but they often dropped in for meeting, and once or twice Sam had been moved to speak.

Ulen did not worship easily when he had a decision to make; the job wasn't finished and worshipping meant taking time from it. He did not feel that he could even ask for help but that he must sit quietly, with the load upon him, and watch it and himself. He must first do his best, with an open heart. The help he had received until then would carry him if he really did his best. Later he would give thanks, and if his spirit was quiet in what he had done his asking would be worship; if he failed it would be supplication.

In the hour of silence he tried to piece together the lives of Jon and Sara as they had lived them and to imagine their reach and pressure. Then ahead, into the future they might expect. Now again, in re-imagination — not in terms of reach and pressure and promise, but of spirit and awakening and rebirth. Where were the fragile signs? Jon's face on the stand, the precise placing and purpose of his lie; Sara's uncertainty whether to follow him and crying in her failure; the pace and the circumstances of their crime. No use looking for the beginning of a new order in them unless it was really there; to invent it for himself was sheerest sentimentality. Painfully he searched his mental image of their faces and of their small unheeding actions. So little to go on, and yet so much, if he could see it. He could not stop to feel compassion for them. Crisply and awarely he must use, in the effort to find their death and rebirth and growth again, the process of a constant re-imagining. This endless rebuilding of a life he could help by fairly becoming part of it. Those who stayed dead or helplessly alive he had to hand over to the doctors and prison technicians, such as they were. His court was cluttered with such cases, and he had no business with them, beyond taking part in the determination of their guilt or innocence. Those who dared to die and live again but had lost their way a little in the process needed a trial to show them back to clarity. And when they saw their way and he could see that they saw it, he could withdraw from judging them, since they were doing that themselves. The greatest judging lay in knowing when to say no word at all.

He looked out of the window with muffled attention. The limb of the great oak was still in the July heat and the faces around him were composed in demure serenity. These Quakers were seeking the rebirth into a fully Christlike life. Such a far cry to the young Sanders and their savage combat in the ambush that life had set for them. Their rebirth might be only a tiny step; it was usually so in his cases, even after such awful pain as theirs, and the temptation was great to expect a step commensurate with the suffering. But he did not think that it was ever his business to measure the length of the new step, provided it was taken cleanly. It might grow to greater ones. How to tell was the puzzle. At times the sign came even during trial; it might have been so with Sara, after she had failed Jon and realized that she had. But she had righted herself quickly, almost too quickly. Most likely Bardelman was right: that's what genius does to a person, and in a sense society has to pay for what it gets from genius. No easy life to be one or to be near one. Bardelman could draw her fire and absorb it in his own; he seemed to have enough of it, Ulen thought with an inner chuckle, the crusty old coot. He was just the kind of human piledriver that could knock away her rough corners and make something wonderful of her. Her parents had made a mess of it, and here was Bardelman itching for the chance to take over; it might mean a new life for her under the kind of despot that she needed. He wished there were a gentler way, but she was hard, and he had to work with the materials and tools at hand.

Jon's case seemed clear to him. He hadn't understood at first why the boy had testified, obviously against Martin's instructions. It looked like a quixotic young effort to shield his sister and get credit for himself, but he had seemed indifferent to that when he left the stand without swagger or self-consciousness, his thin face abstracted. He might be aiming at some other target, and without him the trial would have lacked the story of their dreadful experience. There was a nakedness about deliberate or casual crime that was lacking here; horrible as this crime had been, it looked more like an integument covering deeper reasons and initially better purposes than a separate deed. The more he saw of crime the more he thought of it as an ill but protective skin to be ripped off by expert hands capable of curing some causative illness beneath. The number of those hands was increasing, directed by inquiring minds which refused to accept man's errors as coming from inexplicable wickedness. Jon had managed somehow to turn the terrible business to account. Ulen felt sure of him, but Sara still eluded him.

Someone was speaking. Ulen listened with a muted ear, the tide of words washing intermittently against his consciousness. It was an earnest young man that had been moved to arise and give his testimony, and now he was bringing Augustine to help him. The words suddenly came through clearly to Ulen, for the young man had raised his little book and begun to read:

"And being made spiritual he judges all things which are to be judged and yet is judged himself by no man. Spiritual persons judge spiritually, not only those that are spiritually set over but they also that spiritually are subject to those that are set over them, since in this way didst Thou make man male and female, in Thy grace spiritual, where there is neither male nor female, neither Jew nor Grecian, neither bond nor free. So man, though now spiritual, ought to be a doer of the law and not a judge. Neither does he judge of that distinction of spiritual and carnal men who are known unto Thine eyes, O our God, and have not yet discovered themselves to us by their works; nor does he, though spiritual, judge the unquiet people of the world, for what has he to do with judging them that are without, knowing not which of them shall hereafter come into the sweetness of Thy grace and which continue in the perpetual bitterness of ungodliness?"

His mind lowered over the words. It was the unquiet people of the world that he had to judge, the distinction between the spiritual and the carnal that he had to make. Or was it? Perhaps it was the wisdom of the old saint that the unquiet people judged themselves and that his province was to discover their works in order to find out whether they had. At once the case took on a new appearance in his mind. It became a shape, without pressure or impressions or bits of testimony contending within him for significance. The details fell away until it lay whole and quiet in his mind's eye, like an iceberg from whose tip above the water he had to trace the contours of the hidden mass beneath. It was difficult; he did not know the contours of Jon's and Sara's life except for the tip that had broached the surface before his eyes. He must act with relation to the whole of them, to their entire arc and purpose, and of that he knew very little. He had seen them and their parents, and it had struck him that the children may have been lonely in the stately wilderness of wealth and had to find their own paths in it. The parents seemed withdrawn and out of touch; they had no authority from which to tell him what kind of people their children were.

The little that his senses could tell him was only the outside of the question. Society expected firm justice when it came to murder. Killers must be clapped into jail, and in the ordinary case he could clap them there without compunction, despite his knowing that their past and future went in with them. No better way had yet been found, but that fact made of the current system none the less a process of revenge. He did not fear Jon and Sara as potential menaces to society; they had killed under the sternest provocation, and compared with a confirmed thief they presented hardly any social problem at all. He was sure that they would not repeat their crime, and it would be a most unlikely precedent, as few others would ever be similarly situated. All of these considerations were clear enough. What remained obscure was whether Sara had taken a fresh step forwards from her terrible experience and from the long trail of her past that had led to it. Of Jon he had no final doubt; the affair had torn across the boy's life like a naked belt of electricity and had swirled him into its vacuum. Jon had not directed it, nor had he been destroyed by it, as he might have been. Having been mastered, he emerged a better master of himself. But Sara was different; the key to her was missing.

The meeting had grown silent again and Ulen bent his head, trying to hold the image of the case undisturbed. He tried to recede from it himself and to surround it with as perfect a stillness as he could manage. He wanted to see it as a shape, alone and without attributes. With great effort he held it so for as long as he could; then he slowly raised his head and let his ideas about it return as they would. The first that came was the sight of Sara weeping, and like a gathering cloud the picture of her failure grew until it filled his mind and rested there. Her failure was the measure of her fresh step; had she been strong she would have proved herself to be unregenerate. Ulen stiffened his arms and rested his weight upon his hands. The idea satisfied him. She had been incapable of sacrifice, but that was all right; sacrifice was too close to willing death, and he mistrusted it. Those who really give themselves sacrifice nothing, but create. She had had to fail. The unquiet people of the world will ultimately judge themselves if one will give them time. He looked up quizzically at the members on the facing bench. They were shaking hands, and the meeting stirred and awoke.

Ulen and his wife joined the Willens at the door and walked home with them. Artema's house was on the way, and she and Morris were reading under the oak tree, waiting for them. The bulldog lay with his wrinkled, blunt head on his paws, looking as if he had just been run over by something. Sam's house was not far beyond, the last one in a row that stretched like a finger from the city, and although he had no trees of his own he could see some, and he thought that seeing them was as good as owning them, and less taxable. There was a tiny yard behind the house, and he and Ida had fitted it out with a gay awning, some flagstones, and a few privet bushes with blue morning-glories between them. It faced the woods and was cool. To the awning in due time Ida brought lunch, with iced tea that tinkled, and they ate in steamer chairs or on great bollard-like leather cushions.

"Sorry I couldn't get Nathan and Councill," Sam remarked. "Councill said he had to take a leg off at one and couldn't be bothered."

"Nathan will be found in our pool with the children," Mrs. Ulen said. "You'd better come over for a swim this afternoon. This is the kind of day the thing was made for."

The others assented and stretched themselves. Artema looked at Ulen.

"I noticed in the newspapers," she said in a resigned tone, "that you have been trying a case. I presume we should await the worst."

He grinned. He had the habit of trying his most interesting criminal cases on his friends, to see what sentence they would give. It made pleasant social entertainment and he often picked up a helpful point of view.

"All right," he answered. "I'll talk."

"That is good," Artema murmured. "It means that he has decided on what he is going to do. Otherwise he would be miserable company and say nothing for several hours."

Mrs. Ulen bent a solemn eye upon her. "It is horrible," she remarked, "to have a woman friend who knows my husband as well as I do. It removes from me the sense of dangerous but futile competition that delights women."

Artema giggled.

"As his former office wife," she responded with a sweeping bow, "I know only his virtues. It is the surest guarantee against falling in love with any man."

"Well, anyway – " Ulen began hurriedly. He told them the story in detail and purposely built it up as an insoluble conflict between the rights of society and the needs of Jon and Sara, drawing a little on his imagination to outline their background as he had divined it. It made dramatic telling, and the group was silent for some time after he had finished. Finally Morris shook his head. Odd, Ulen thought, seeing him about to say something, how the weakest among us usually gives his opinion first. Morris's opinion was flat.

"I vote for a stiff sentence," he said, clearing his throat. "It should be twenty years, I think. A killing like that is cold-blooded, despite the jam they were in. It was blind rage, which makes it bad, and the victim was helpless, which makes it worse. I'd be as tough as I could be on violence. It may be hard luck, but they have no one but themselves to blame." He looked around from one to the other for support, but they were staring at the trees and did not move.

Ulen looked at Artema, who cocked her head pertly.

"I stand mute," she said, challenging him. "Knowing you for your virtues, I knew what you would make up your mind to do before you knew yourself. With that broad hint I refuse to be a Cassandra before this assemblage."

Sam studied his shoe.

"I say one year in jail and nine years' probation," hc drawled reflectively, after glancing up to see if it was his turn to speak. "You can't do less. I looked it up once and found that nobody convicted of murder has ever been put only on probation. Sad but true. One to ten for the boy and the Women's Reformatory for the girl."

"Ida?" Ulen inquired.

Ida was silent for a little while.

"Well," she said finally, "I believe that a judge must have some theory behind his punishments. I'd try to take some measurements first, if I were in your place. I think everybody's life has an arc; it goes in some direction at a certain speed and with a certain force. To break the arc is a serious matter, and sending a person to jail might break it beyond repair, or it might not. Some people break their own arcs when they commit crimes; either that or crime becomes their arc. In those cases I suppose jail is the only thing possible. But if they can patch the break themselves, why should you break it again? Back of them is the greater arc of society, but it's so big that no one can tell where it's going, except generally, and it isn't likely to break under one blow, particularly one as unusual as this. I suppose a judge has to have some assurance against repetition." She paused, hunting for a way on.

"Where would you look for it?" Ulen asked.

Ida raised her eyes to him candidly.

"That's your business," she said, "and no one can help you with it very much. You look for it in people's faces, in your own spirit, in the confused staccato of living. But most of all you must look for it in the lives of Jon and Sara Sander. I shouldn't vote to keep them in jail an extra day, despite Sam's formidable statistics, but I'm trying to say something beyond that.

"You might let these children go, and ruin them, or you might send them to jail, and not hurt them. I like what the young man read in meeting this morning from St. Augustine, that the best judges don't pass judgment. You don't sentence crimes, you sentence people, and being on the Bench you become part of the force that's directing their lives at a very crucial moment. You're like a wind blowing through a tree; once you take a case and start blowing, so to speak, the result will be yours and no one else's on earth. I can't say it very clearly, but I think that the only helpful vote your friends can give you is a vote of confidence."

"Gosh," said Ulen and got up. "Come on, let's go for a swim."

He had no need to ask his wife for her opinion. She had

given it after the fashion of wives, the night the trial ended. She had read the newspaper account after dinner, swinging her foot slightly and humming a little to herself.

" 'The jurist deferred sentence until Monday,' " she read aloud. "I hate that word jurist. It makes you sound like a totem pole." She put the paper aside and removed her glasses by taking them between thumb and forefinger and twisting her head free. Holding them for a moment in front of her like a sextant she looked at him with a twinkle and then arose. "If you send those children to jail," she remarked, "you should have your head examined."

The afternoon sun was hot, and they drove to Ulen's house in Sam's car. As Mrs. Ulen had predicted, Nathan was already in the pool with Severn and Barbara, his curly hair unaffected by the water and still in full flight to the rear. He was trying to stand on his head on an inflated rubber raft. The children paddled about him with delighted yelps, and Nathan was shouting at the top of his lungs from any position in which he happened to find himself, except when completely submerged, and then great bubbles rose from him. Upon emerging, he was a little farther along in his sentence than when he disappeared.

Severn and Barbara scrambled up the bank when they saw their parents.

"He fell off," Barbara announced, blowing the water from her lips. "He fell off seventeen times. I counted."

"I can do it easy," Severn said, "if I don't try to talk upside down."

Nathan wallowed in the center of the pool and finally came

over to join them. He was a little blown and was content to sit and glisten in the sunshine. Ulen took a plunge and came out to lie down on his back under a tree. He found that Uncle Michael had appeared and was sitting there with Nathan. The pool had been made by damming the outlet from a small basin of land through which a brook ran, and the water lay almost at the foot of a row of willows that let down their branches over it and gave shelter from the sun. The grassy banks ran to the water's edge and the overflow from the pool sang from the far side of the dam.

Nathan regarded Ulen reflectively. When he was quiet his eyes were mature and patient, as though he dressed by preference like a clown. "What are you going to do with the Sander kids?" he asked.

"Nothing. They're all right as they are – now," Ulen added.

Nathan nodded comprehendingly.

"What are you going to say to them?"

"Don't know. It bothers me."

"The less said the better."

Ulen grunted. "That makes it harder."

Nathan was silent for a moment. "You've got to say something very good," he observed. "When you put a man in jail you pass sentence and he understands it. When you let him go you have to pass an essay, for he doesn't understand being let go. You know all about that, I take it."

"I know all about that," Ulen answered. "The public doesn't always understand it either."

"I wouldn't worry too much about the public," Michael put in quietly, "and not too much about your young defendants, for that matter. I hope you've gotten clear about all that by this time. The public is apt to approve an honest and intelligent effort, and your defendants are tougher than you realize. You can't break somebody else's life very easily; within reason it can be bent with considerable freedom. You get needlessly wrought up over the accuracy of your sentences; you're decent enough not to hurt anybody too much, and that's about all that need be avoided or can be.

"It's not the sentence I'm concerned with. It's the whole trial, its tones and its overtones, and what everyone in court will take away with him when it's over. The main difference between tyranny and democracy is courtesy – an attitude of affectionate respect for everything that lives because it lives. If people don't learn that in our courts they won't learn it anywhere, and they must learn it if we are to become a race of gentlefolk. A sympathetic and courteous trial is more important than strict accuracy of sentence, which can become sentimental if you don't watch it."

There was a pause before Nathan spoke.

"The jury recommended mercy. That ought to help," he said.

"It's no help," Ulen growled. "I refuse to wheeze about mercy."

Nathan shrugged and got to his feet to join the children.

"There are worse things than mercy in this wicked world," he said. "I admit you have to get pretty far down to think so. It's the death cry of the hunted and don't you forget it."

"I won't," said Ulen. "That's why I don't like it."

He raised his head and watched Nathan take a little run and land flat on his stomach in the pool beside Severn, throwing a silver spray of water over Ida while she climbed up the bank. She shook herself and came over to where Ulen was lying, the drops shining like translucent pearls on her dark skin.

"Is it man or elephant?" she said, looking at Nathan with a laugh, and sat down.

"Either," Ulen answered. "Actually, a wounded man, I should say. He believes in mercy."

"That's too bad," Ida said. "It hasn't any meaning if you relax enough."

He looked at her quickly.

"What do you find to take its place?"

Ida flexed her big toes and extended the others.

"You should know," she answered slowly. "Are you giving the Sander children mercy?"

"Not if I can help it."

"Then what are you giving them?"

"I'm trying to see them as they are and then accept them."

"And after that?"

"Try to do what's best for them."

"Which takes faith, doesn't it?" Ida asked, rubbing her chin against her clavicle. He grunted affirmatively.

"Well, there you are," she said, switching her head around to look at him directly. "Things in their proper order, and the prayer of my people as well – to be known, to be accepted, and to be accorded faith."

"One thing left out," Michael observed. She looked at him questioningly.

"What is it?"

"The quality of what happens after that," he said. "It isn't good automatically. We're a self-conscious people, and there's still another step for us to take when we deal with others. You're not, and therefore acceptance is enough when you deal with others. But when we both deal with ourselves there is the same extra step ahead."

He paused, his eyes slanted downward, and they let him think a minute.

"It's a question," he went on, "a question that won't ever be answered, but it will transmute into a growing calm that is like a charged acceptance. What Art Thou: What Am I?"

"How does that fit, Ida?" Ulen asked.

"I won't answer directly," she said, lifting her eyes to Severn, who was floating about the pool on his head, "but I'll tell you a story that you don't know about your son. Children can manage these things naturally and more simply.

"Do you remember the night when Sam and I came out here for the first time about ten years ago? It was some committee you were having to dinner and we were all dressed up. Sam had on his dinner jacket and I was in a long black dress. Well, we went upstairs to put away our things and started back down the hall. It is broken by three steps in the middle, as you know. Severn was two then and he had apparently set forth on some adventure of his own at the same time we left your room. He came from the nursery at the other end of the hall, and we could see him weaving along, waving his fat arms and putting his feet down flat and sudden. He was stark naked and absorbed in the problem of the floor in front of him. He reached the bottom of those three steps just as we reached the top. Involuntarily we stopped and stood still. It is always quite a moment for us, you know, with white children.

"Seeing four large feet about on the level of his eyes, he began raising his head until he saw our faces. We held our breath when we should have made it easy for him, but there was no need. With his head so far back that it almost toppled off, he took us all in, carefully and solemnly; then he hoisted it forward, put one foot uncertainly on the lowest step, and held out his hands to us.

"I led him into the nursery, where he sat down abruptly on the floor and kept gazing at me with his round inscrutable face until I was almost out of sight down the stairs. Just as I turned the corner I waved at him and he waved back. I felt that the three of us had been equals in all of the experience in life that is important."

On Monday Ulen disposed of Fennel first, wasting little time on him. He asked Sara enough about her relations with him to get the picture, and turned to Fennel.

"You have to pay for sex, you know," he said to him, "either in cash on delivery or in time or affection. Even casual sex takes a chunk out of a woman or nails one on. No woman can take it and go scot free. A man can, and therefore he must pay in one way or another. You should know that.

"You cannot pay Miss Sander anything, but in a sense you can liquidate her debt. I hope you will feel that the situation has sentenced you and not a man in a black robe. She spent three months in jail awaiting trial for murder. Had you met your obligation in the beginning, she might not have killed the child you begot upon her. The least you can do is to match the time society has taken from her. Three months in the County prison."

He looked at Jon and Sara for a moment and then addressed them.

"That is all the time society is going to take from you two. I must represent society as well as you, and I take the responsibility for believing that it will not suffer any more at your hands. It may benefit greatly. It has, however, a sentence of its own beyond any that I could impose. Your road through school and college and in business, Jon, will not be so easy for your having once been convicted of murder. You will have to live it down and at first that may be difficult. The young are as cruel as they are conservative. But I trust you, and I have been your judge. I shall let you go because you have been strong; you have been able to master this situation and yourself as well.

"I shall also let you go, Sara, not because you have been strong but because you have been weak. Something has at last mastered you and you needed to be mastered. But you have still to serve out the sentence of being an artist, and the public can be as cold and unnoticing as you can be the opposite. The greatest sentence you will have to serve, however, is the knowledge that you let your brother down, and if you can live beyond that and forgive yourself you will be great indeed. And you will find, I think, that he will say no word. He is beyond you as an artist, although he can do nothing with his hands. He took the stand, not to protect you but to protect your right to protect yourself. He gave himself. You took yourself. Having genius, you probably always will, but you will tire of it; it is the surest road to boredom, which is the purgatory in which most self-conscious people live. You have by far the heavier sentence. If you can serve it and emerge, you will be a great artist.

"Remember the closing words of your indictment, before you were put on trial. It is the attitude of the law towards its prisoners, as I believe it is the attitude of life towards those who are about to live it. 'May God send you a safe deliverance.'

"You are free now. Sentence is suspended."

IX

The Bay

ULEN WENT to the Bay every summer for as much vacation as he could manage. It held an old magic for him and restored his energy after the winter's work, with its ceaseless flood of people and their problems, had left him dry and blunted his resources. The northern woods and water filled him again. Everyone is a foreigner to another's troubles, and it is good to store up reserves against them that are as slow and direct as the processes of earth. Such a background gives him margin to work in — an abundance of time and space, which grow noisier the more narrowly they are tethered and quieter the more they are allowed to widen to the place where a man's life appears to stand still against their imperceptible march.

That even the eternal might itself be relative did not concern Ulen while he walked up the mountain that stood sentinel above the Bay. It would be a foot lower and the earth a yard farther from the sun in a hundred years, but he could by no effort become aware of the minute tumult in the cosmic war of attrition, and he felt that there was a purpose in his having been made insensitive to it. He needed silence and came to the mountain early in his visit to restore his acuity to it. The city had dulled him by its steady roar imposed upon the delicate layers of sound that create silence, and he had to renew at once his ability to distinguish the very few that could be separated. At first it would be a matter for the eye, looking at immobility from afar and bringing it closer without disturbance; then for the ear, removing sounds one by one from the background, which allowed them to be heard, until only the background remained; at last for the spirit, sensing a darker void beneath the silence, until silence ceased to be external and grew to be the retentive depths of the soul. Finally the sense of retention would withdraw, slowly and after great effort, and while it receded light would come, as from a formless and invisible sun. Silence would then become peace.

The path lay over rocks and through the woods. It led first over the sharp nose of a foothill, a hard core that had become aquiline from butting against the retreating ice. Cairns and old blobs of paint marked the way, and the underbrush grew low and tight on the steep face of the hill. Above this the path levelled and the woods came, soft underfoot with pine-needles or broken here and there by granite ledges like the backs of broaching whales. In southern climates pines are the hottest trees that grow, but in the north they give warmth and accent to the forest, and stand like pillars supporting it. Here the roots were strong but shallow and gripped the earth with knotted cords. In the long-needled pines the wind was a deep contralto. In the hemlock and spruce it was a brush, but the deciduous trees rustled like sheets of paper, and the birches fidgeted. Birch behaved differently from all other trees, as if their pallor gave them special privileges. In fair weather their leaves bent downwards under wind, but at the first breath of storm they grew pale when the leaves blew upwards and showed their lighter green beneath. So long as there was a breath of air they rustled; in falling weather they dripped incontinently; in sunlight they waved about and shone. They were more like human flesh and blood than most trees, with pliant skin and a moist toughness in the wood that gave them suppleness but rotted quickly after death. In life they danced fastidiously and gave alarms.

Ulen reached the last face of cliffs and clambered up to the niche of rock below the summit that gave him a natural chair in which to rest and eat his lunch. Cups of rock lichen made a cushion under him, and he stretched himself contentedly and looked down. The level stand of hardwood just below the cliffs was an apron of light green across the dark pine forest. The thin white fingers of the birch shot through it and waved their hankerchiefs among the lumbering oak and maple. A seagull glided over it. Strange to look down on a bird flying. He could see gusts of the offshore breeze sweep across the hardwood until they reached the gull, which kept level by rocking gently without a movement of its wings. Its hoarse and lonely cry reached him faintly. He raised his eyes to the Bay and the maze of islands lying in it. The calm surface looked harder than the rounded tufts of land coated with forest save for hands and feet of rock that seemed to clench the water. Here and there were naked reefs, one of them rising starkly in the middle of the Bay. It was called The Horns, but it was the spindles on either end of it that gave purpose to the name. Without them it could have lain low in the water, ugly and nameless. Far to the left were the Wooden Plate Shoals, a group of small islands which cormorants and gulls had chosen as a nesting ground. The birds had stripped them of every blade of grass and there remained only a few skeletons of denuded trees on whose branches the cormorants' nests hung in clusters. It was a sign of bad weather when the birds came in unusually large numbers and settled there, beaks to the wind. Wooden Plate weather, the natives called it, and it meant three days of rain and gray boulders of waves rolling in from the northeast. In front of him the village sat with its feet in the water of the tiny, crooked harbor.

Ulen ate his lunch and lay back against the sloping rock. Fresh from the city, he was very tired, and its roar still rumbled in his ears. He began slowly to pick out the sounds about him and to separate them. He could tell the kinds of trees behind him by the wind in their branches, and he fastened his attention upon each one in turn until he could hear it alone. Then he sought the shorter and rarer sounds – the cry of the gull, the creaking of branches, the distant clang of a bell-buoy. He tried to reach out for the whistler off Seven Acre Ledge. He could see it but the wind was wrong. The effort gave him a little area of silence to listen to, a space between the other sounds. Too hard just now, tired as he was. He closed his eyes, trying to retain the image of the Bay, and discovered that he could not see it three-dimensionally in his mind's eye but only flat, like a picture. He opened his eyes suddenly at the realization that perspective was a property of the eye alone and that it could be imagined only as a concept. He thought about it for a minute and closed his eyes again to test it. He became aware of the droning of a bee, and followed the trail of sound as far as he could. It did not stop but faded into tone, so slowly that silence did not come but rather grew in its place. He seemed to be riding out to the end of the little trail and drifting in again with the quiet. He knew that he was dozing, and he was content to let consciousness break up and float away, as ice leaves a lake. He must not try to hold it or consciousness would snap back again. He must be passively aware, prepared to dwindle. Silence was now a wing around him, but it melted and darkness came, and the void.

When he awoke it was late afternoon. The sky was alive with cotton-headed clouds, and between them the slanting sunlight lay like long swords on the landscape. High above them were little cirrus clouds, bright yellow in the ebbing spate of light, and bent like birds' wings. There would have been storm except for the high pressure that broke the heavy clouds and localized the showers. There were several squalls around the horizon, and he saw that one had settled on the highest peak of the range of hills across the Bay. A gray mushroom of raincloud sat upon it and slowly turned to lavender dust when the sun lanced through it. Behind this curtain the mountain lost its corruscation of pine and rock and looked sculptured, like the head of an elephant. The foreshore, free of rain and hidden from the sun, was an indigo band across the foot of the mountain, and farther on a cup in the hills was filled with tawny yellow light. The main islands were also dark, but those behind still had the sun on them and stood out in deep gold. When he reached the town it was twilight, the western sky green behind the black lace of pines.

Outside the post office he met Paul Snow. Paul was a lobsterman and pulled a hundred traps daily from late March until the end of December, if the Bay froze over, and without stopping at all, if it didn't. He was small in the head and broad in the beam, and seemed to have become partly crustacean himself. One looked furtively at his hands, half expecting to see teeth between thumb and forefinger, and his back was bent stiffly, as if there were shell beneath his clothes. He had a stentorian voice that could be heard across the village, and he used it as other people used their foghorns or sirens. Except when out in a fog and requiring it for professional purposes, he directed it at Mrs. Snow from various prodigious distances to indicate that he wanted his supper the instant he arrived. At close quarters he spoke in a whisper, having no middle range between a full-throated bellow and a muffled rasp.

The result of their meeting was an invitation to go out the next day in Paul's boat. Ulen enjoyed doing this. In few other places could he come so near the point where people and the elements and the country met, the lowest common denominator of a free man and a free earth. Working about a hundred hours a week, Paul made a modest living and was pleased with it. He had chosen this incredible labor and found freemasonry rather than discontent among his fellow lobstermen. Attempts to organize them into a union had failed signally but quietly; the labor representative who had been sent to try it was picked up in the middle of the Bay by a Coast Guard cutter a day or two later in an open rowboat without oars, and the lobstermen looked vaguely out to sea when asked about it. It made Ulen wonder a little. Perhaps a voluntary return to the farm, the hills, and the water would bring a simpler way of life, with harder work and greater personal happiness. It was just possible.

They met next morning at Paul's house. It was filled and surrounded with lobster traps and accessories – net, cord, bricks, and a reserve of lath. In the kitchen, like a heart in a body, sat Mrs. Snow, with the air of having won by main force enough space for cooking and washing and of never intending to leave it for fear it would fill up with Paul's gear if she turned her back. Paul looked like something that automatically fills up vacuums. His boat was like his house, only more so, and looked as if he had been turned inside out and left lying about. Brown bilge water oozed over the floorboards when the boat tilted. Bricks to ballast the traps were piled in the corners. The deck had as many scales on it as a fish. There was an open barrel of salted herring and one of redfish, which Paul used for bait. The redfish had been bought from a store where the fillets had been removed, but the remaining meat and the heads were enough for his purposes. They had mournful faces, rather like bloodhounds, and the red color of their flesh gave them a look of deep and melancholy embarrassment. A sack of salt lay on the after deck, and there were empty baskets for the day's catch.

Paul was clad in an oilskin apron, rubber boots, a torn shirt, and a cap with a vizor ten inches long. Finding that the boat would not start readily, he tested the battery by throwing on the switch with one hand and holding the other hand between the terminals. Judging from the howl that rose to Ulen on top of the cabin, there appeared to be sufficient current. The boat started at length and they headed out a small reach of backwater that Paul used as a short cut to his traps. It was shallow and Paul peered over the side, tempering his motor. "Water's a mite thin here," he remarked. "Channel ain't much more than a crease I've worn in these rocks with my keel." They drifted over the ledge into deeper water and resumed their speed until they approached the traps. Paul hauled them in by passing the buoy line over a revolving spindle attached to his engine. Setting his tiller at such an angle that the boat ambled slowly in a circle, he emptied the trap, baited it, and shoved it overboard, watching it for a moment while it slithered down into the green undergloom with a bristle of crisp salt bubbles. He threw the small lobsters over the side and they disappeared almost at once, swimming jerkily backwards with their tails and letting their legs and claws stream out loosely in front of them. All of this was completed by the time the boat had finished its circle; Paul was never idle or hurried, and he was never compelled to do two necessary things at once. Between one trap and the next he attended to his lobsters. Those on the borderline of legal size he measured with a small brass ruler – from eyesocket to end of carapace. "Too small enough, as the fella said," he announced once, and the lobster described a long arc seawards. He glanced up shyly. Ulen grinned and Paul eyed him wickedly while he rinsed his hands from the bit of hose that discharged the water from his engine.

"Tell you a good one on you summer people," he went on. "Seems there was a girl who hadn't been in these parts before, and she found an old fisherman sitting on a piling. 'Lots of quaint people up here,' she says to him. 'Well, yes,' he says, 'in a manner of speaking there is, but they most all of them go home by Labor Day.' Heard it myself," he concluded, and returned to his lobsters. On being picked up they flapped their tails and waved their vast claws frighteningly, but once they had spread them backwards to full reach they stayed there. At that point Paul took each claw quietly in his hand, pegged it, and placed the lobster in a basket. Over each layer he threw a piece of wet kelp that had been dragged up with the traps.

Ulen surveyed this from the top of the cabin, which was the only place in the boat for him to sit. There was little he need do but look appreciative and nod, for Paul talked incessantly and like most men who work alone was given more to declaration than inquiry. The Bay was his museum as well as his workshop, and his speech had grown quaint through finding small quick words for small quick discoveries. When he spoke of broader forces like wind and tide and storm his language broadened with it. To Ulen he was a piece of the Bay that had become human and could make vocal the laws and processes beneath its quiet face. Strange, how the manifestations of those precise laws were clustered at the opposite ends of perception, like red giant stars and white dwarfs, leaving little between except room to be casual: room where winds blew, trees grew crookedly, the restless sea heaved—and lobsters moved from place to place on urges of their own, Paul was saying. He couldn't understand why they did but he managed to keep up with them. Living by approximations, he measured things by bits or mites or some; pounds and gallons and miles were not laws but facts too accurate to be trusted. No room for play and the slow growth of instinctive judgment by which the fitful rushes of Nature might be outwitted. But he could judge a coming storm or the set of a current in a fog, matching their imprecision against the flow of his experience and reaching balance.

Paul's tide of observation flowed under Ulen's reverie as placidly as the water past the boat. Now and then he found a treasure in one of his traps and his enormous paw would approach Ulen's face: a sand dollar, he was saying, they're few and marked right even if you look close enough; here's a sculpin in this one, and he held out the big ugly fish, handy with those spikes, so watch out; a starfish leg, and he arose to teach, letting the boat amble twice in its circle – it was growing a new starfish, as the starfish that had lost it was growing a new leg. One trap yielded a colossal lobster of four or five pounds and Ulen shouted congratulations. Paul laughed. "Old friend of mine," he observed. "Name's Bertha. Put her back in the bank and draw interest." He pointed to the markings on the middle of the creature's tail that denoted sex and turned her over to show Ulen the roe. "State's lobster," he concluded, lowering her over the side and pausing to watch her flap awkwardly out of sight. He leaned over farther to rinse his hand in the seawater and swept his eyes briefly around the horizon; wind would change after a bit, he said, he'd skip these traps and go to the end of his run so they'd work back easier. Ulen settled himself for the trip up the coast, easing his back as comfortably as he could against the short mast. He couldn't tell much about the weather and asked Paul how he knew. Paul surveyed the ragged sky. "Don't know for sure," he said, "but there's two or three little handbills up there. They'll leak a trifle before they blow over." He came forward and took up the sculpin again. "He'll puff way up if you rub his belly," he observed, taking the fish's head between his legs and rubbing the tough yellow skin. The sculpin gave a few gasps and swelled obscenely. Paul threw it overboard. "Now he'll float," he went on. "With a mouth as big as that you'd think he could belch it right up, but he can't. Seagull will come along and punch a hole in it for him."

It was a leathery kind of day, the fog belting in across the mountains before an east wind and the Bay alive with a little choppy sea. Just off The Horns they came up behind a seal swimming. Since the animal could not hear very well, it was not until it turned its large eyes and saw them that it took fright and was gone in a white blister of water. A school of porpoises arched their dorsals and rolled below again. At times the boat was very near the rocks that fell sharply into the deep cold water. They seemed to pull the waves up to their chins and throw them off again when their hood of bladderwrack taughtened with the receding water. A red medusa floated by, trailing its evil streamers. The handbills began to leak a little. The mountain where Ulen had been the day before reared itself from the shoreline ahead. He had found remoteness there, but from the boat the mountain was withdrawn. Majesty is not found below eye level or contentment above it. Loneliness flows uphill and companionship down, and wherever people are together their gradients can be observed. Feeling quite satisfied at the moment, he had no need to look to the mountain for help and found it haughty and aloof.

The weather changed during the last part of the trip, as Paul had said it would, and the wind veered abruptly from the east into the southwest, chasing the fog before it. Then it fell into a flat calm and only a slight groundswell remained when Paul left Ulen at his dock and made off up the harbor to finish his traps.

Ulen found Julia playing on the small stony apron between the headlands near their house that served as a beach. It was a small and sheltered place where a little girl could play safely. The tiny stretch of pebbles was guarded by solid ledges so matted with seaweed as to look at low tide like sheepdogs. Above high-water mark they sloped downward from the trees, as if escaping from a tunnel beneath the forest. Upshore a mile or so Malay Island Light sat fat and white upon its rock. Julia played by the hour on the beach, and Ulen, sitting curled up on a ledge and feeling himself adrift on the flowing salt air, held together only by his fishing pants and old leather jacket, watched her closely as the summers went by. Even during the summer when she was a year old she had played there happily, and as the years passed, the beach became her empire and she could be trusted on it. Most of the time she spent on her haunches, examining minute matters of importance – the shape and color of stones, a dead snail of uncertain odor, laces of dry seaweed. Now and then she would straighten herself and look out at the Bay, her nose pressed upward in a squint and her blue eyes miniature bays joined inwardly to the large one. It's all right, he said to himself, it will always be all right; I need only guide a little. Their wave-lengths were very nearly the same, despite their ages, and the difference in years was largely a matter of tempo. Julia was a small but constant gale of wind that seemed particularly blowy when she was at rest, but in motion she caught up to it and neutralized it. Her most accurate impressions came when she was active, and she could no more think while doing nothing than Ulen could think while strenuously exerting himself.

He came over to her from the dock. She was playing near a long narrow cleft in the ledge that bored into one side of the beach. It ran inland about thirty feet and was five or six feet deep. One wall was vertical and the other sloped to form an angle with it at the bottom. Long fronds of seaweed grew there, dark greenish-brown above the yellow floor of barnacles. Ulen liked to watch them flow backwards and forwards, circling to their full length while the groundswell poured through the cleft. He had seen dancers try to do it, hands over heads and bodies bent like the central stalk in an oriental flower arrangement. He thought the seaweed did it better, and wondered why anything not born in seawater should try it.

Julia bounded up and down the ledge. She had a convex upper lip the shape of a scimitar in profile, and it gave her an air of decision somewhat greater than she really had. She looked straight at things until she had seen all she wanted and she did not speak until she had finished looking. When Ulen glanced up from watching the seaweed he saw that she had squatted on her heels beside a tide-pool and was examining a small jellyfish, her body far down between her knees. The jellyfish was graceful but obviously uncomfortable. Ulen bent over her.

"This jellyfish dances," Julia announced, "but I can dance much faster."

"You can't move all over at once," Ulen said, "the way he can."

"Yes, I can," she shouted. She jumped up and executed a wild manoeuvre. Ulen was imperturbable.

"Back didn't move," he observed. Julia redoubled her efforts.

"Stomach didn't move," he said, running his finger down her spine. "That's your backbone. When you move it your stomach gets stiff, and when you move your stomach your backbone gets stiff. People can't be loose and keep their arms and legs and head going at the same time. If they could they'd look sick. That's why it's silly to watch people dance after you've seen seaweed or a jellyfish. So long as they have hard round heads sticking out from the tops of them they won't be able to flow and there's no use trying. They may be graceful as people but not as a cosmic phenomenon."

Julia had her own ways of bringing him back to earth. She wrinkled up her nose and swung her arms briskly, thinking.

"The island is closer today," she observed.

He looked at it. It was a small island, half a mile from shore, and the pines that grew upon its rocky base gave it the look of a sleeping animal with its hair on end. It was true that the island did peculiar things. In fog it retreated to a vast distance, but on a sunny day when the low tide increased the height of its base and shortened the distance between it and the shore, it loomed almost on top of them.

"Some day it will come very close all by itself," Julia went on. "You watch."

"I'll watch," he replied.

"It will come tomorrow," said Julia with finality.

"It's likely to come at any time," Ulen said evenly. "Islands never go away but they do trot about, and there's no telling."

"I'll run when I see it," Julia said, putting an arm around his thigh.

"Oh, no need to do that," he replied. "You won't see it coming. You'll be playing and when you look up it will be there, right beside you. It's a way they have. But it won't scare you. When you see it you'll know what to do."

"What?" she asked.

"Um," he said. "I'm going to sit down. You just wait and see."

He drew her away and they walked across the ledge to the beach. He stretched himself at full length and allowed Julia to take off her shoes and wade. He lay and listened to the swell that moved the stones with its wash. There was the curving hiss of water that never quite became tone, and beneath the hiss a scattering cascade of clean hollow sounds when the receding water tumbled the pebbles upon each other. He closed his eyes to hear it and fix it in his mind. He opened them suddenly at a cry from Julia. She was lifting herself from her heels and looking toward him, pointing with one hand.

The island lay nestled against the shore, one of its rocky shelves only a few feet from her. Ulen felt called upon to do something.

"Well," he said encouragingly. "There it is. Now what do you think of that?"

Julia ran towards him from the shallow water where she had been wading, a thumb in her mouth, but stopped when she saw no alarm in her father and turned back to the island. The air was still and the sunlight glanced from the water in little white flashes. The island made no sound save for the groundswell that rose and fell like silk upon its rocks. The low shelf was an inviting ramp. Ulen saw that it fascinated Julia but was larger than her small stock of courage. He realized that the island had done all it could, coming so quietly, and that the rest was up to him. Besides, he believed that magic could be robbed of its guile if taken in stride. He got up. Julia had not yet found her tongue and took his proferred hand with a hot eagerness.

"Come along, Mrs. 'Opkins," he said. "When islands arrive like this they expect to be boarded. Over we go."

He helped Julia into her shoes, seeing that the island's ledge was so close to their own that they could easily step over to it. Julia gave him a penetrating look, and seeing his face tranquil forgot that there was anything odd in the situation. They crossed to the ramp with a jump and walked up it. Almost at once the woods closed about them, but the sunlight fell in shafts upon a path edged with fern and bunchberries. The tops of the pines made a dark roof above the gray tangle of lower branches that had died for lack of sun, and silence hung in shrouds.

Julia scuffed the pine-needles with her feet, and the sun made bronze of the hair above her stub of neck. They walked on for some time without saying anything. There were occasions when Ulen felt a lack of ready conversation with a four-year-old, and he did not always try to bridge the distance.

The silence grew a little long and he looked about him for something to comment upon. He began to see plants and wildflowers, and was surprised to find that their names came to him readily. There was pipsissewa and vetch, and when he stooped over to push aside some dead leaves he saw the rattlesnake plantain that he had hoped to find there. Reindeer and Jerusalem moss. Wood sage, bergamot, squawroot and Indian pipe. He announced them with relish, pleased to find that he knew them. Must have been studying them recently, but he couldn't remember when. The woods had grown quite dark, and the darkness seemed to grip him before easing and lifting again. He walked along, groping a little, but his knees were stiff, and when he reached down to see a flower more closely his hand looked small and bent. His head felt lower and farther out than was quite comfortable, and he was lonely. Couldn't imagine how he got out there all by himself. Strange. I feel twenty years older, he said to himself glumly, and then remembered. Funny how faint it was: Julia was with him once in a wood like this.

"That's right, Daddy, it was here, at this spot."

He wasn't sure that he heard it. The voice seemed to float to him from a little distance. Yes, it was here, and she was a little girl, with only a stub of neck. Then he heard laughter, light and clear now, right beside him. The forest that lay about him like a dim cathedral grew brighter. He looked up sharply and saw her, his first glance falling on her hair. It was bronze and it rippled where the sun struck it. She shook it and showed her neck; it was not stubby but long and graceful. He saw that she was looking at him and seemed to be waiting for him. But he didn't know. She was tall and slender, and her hands were folded quietly against the front of her plain white dress.

"I don't know," he said querulously, turning towards the path again. "There are so many places that look alike."

The loneliness swelled and the forest grew dimmer.

"Those plants were here, though," he added, half to himself. "I told her their names, some of them."

She took his arm quietly and his mind cleared. She laughed and shook him gently.

"Such long words, Daddy. Pipsissewa and plantain and bergamot, of all things. I was only four, you silly old thing."

"You were cross," he said severely.

"I wasn't either."

"You were too. You thought you were going to see an Indian or something, and I had to go scrabbling about like that in the bushes."

"How on earth did you know that?" she asked.

"Once upon a time," he answered, frowning at the way his voice bleated, "I was four. All I can remember of my father at that time is that when I sat on his lap he was only an enormous head with a pair of hands like sides of beef, and when I walked with him he was nothing but two legs thumping along like destiny beside me. Such a monster could not possibly see anything or understand it if he did. When he punished me it was like a clap of thunder that was having a good time annoying itself: it scared me and sometimes it hurt, but it had nothing to do with me, really. Now that you've grown up you can see how it is."

He gave her a sidelong glance, suddenly doubtful. It was strange how his awareness of her came and went, clear one minute and hazy the next.

"Or can you?" he demanded.

She looked at him but said nothing. The hand on his arm was so light that he could scarcely feel it. He was impelled to go on.

"When you were four I told you whatever occurred to me. I knew I was a monster and decided to behave like the kind of monster you might like. You always seemed to get the idea. You'd screw up your nose and look at me in a certain kind of way. Right here pipsissewa occurred to me, but you kept your head down and wiggled. Then I knew it was Indians or something."

She squeezed his arm.

"That's nice," she said. "Go on."

"There isn't much to go on about. There was so little time." He saw a shadow fall across her face and noticed that her eyes were deep violet. "I loved you very much," he said drily.

She disappeared altogether at that.

"I still do," he said, raising his voice.

"That's better," she said as if nothing had happened. "Only you don't have to shout so."

"I do too," he returned crossly. "I wish you'd stop vanishing."

"I can't help it. It's the way I'm made."

"It's very upsetting," he said. "I'm old but I can adjust to new ideas if they're sensible. Vanishing isn't sensible."

"I don't believe it," she replied. "I'll show you how well you adjust to new ideas."

She pulled him around until he faced her directly and put her cheek against his.

"Oh dear," she murmured, rubbing herself, "whiskers again. Now Daddy, look at me. You know I'm dead, don't you?"

He looked at her quizzically and sniffed. "What on earth are you talking about?" he asked.

"Me," she answered, looking a little hurt. "I said I'm dead."

"All right, you're dead," he remarked. "What about it?"

"Nothing," she said in a rather small voice. "I'm just dead, that's all."

There was a pause and he stroked his chin thoughtfully. They walked along the path for a few moments without speaking. He had the excited feeling that he might be on the edge of a momentous discovery, but he couldn't see how to take full possession of it.

"Well," he said at length, "let's change the subject."

She made a little sound and pressed closer to him. Her eyes were full on him.

"What other subject is there?" she asked.

He was shocked to find that he had no answer and that he was troubled.

"Let's not have a subject," he said. "Do we need one?"

She had been looking at him intently and seemed to approve of him.

"No," she answered, "I don't think we need one, but I wanted to be sure."

He could not rid himself of the impression that she was troubled too, and glanced up at her to confirm it. She was half a head taller than he and her face was sweet, but her eyes were vibrating a little, as if she were coming to a decision. He felt that he must help her if he could, and he spoke seriously.

"What are you trying to tell me, Julia?"

She seemed to be about to say something, but the forest rustled ominously and she looked at her feet in silence. He did not press his question and was surprised to realize that he no longer wanted to. The idea came to him as if it had blown through his skin that the best part of the momentous discovery would be not to know what it was. The need for words had gone, and in its place there was now a full acceptance of her. That was better, and as if she knew it, she leaned over and kissed his ear. They walked on for a long time, the path seeming to walk with them as it wound ahead of them and parted the forest. They must be nearing the water, for there was a breath of mist in the trees; it had caught in the cobwebs between the branches and turned them into tiny lines of chain. A rabbit hopped across the path ahead of them, its spot of cotton bobbing behind it as it looped among the trees and disappeared. Julia turned her eyes full on her father; they were big and dark and filled with the sense of waiting that he had noticed when he first looked at her. Something in him made him speak.

"He isn't really frightened," he said. "His ears are still up."

She gave an almost possessive cry and put her hand on his to hold him close to her. He didn't quite understand why she did that and smiled at her a bit vacantly, squeezing her arm against his side. She read his expression and he thought that he saw a breath of distress cross her face, but it passed and she made no explanation. Again he was aware that he wanted none. The mist grew a little heavier and he found that he was tired, but he felt easier too. He looked about him for a place to rest. Slowly the forest withdrew and in a few minutes they found themselves at the head of a small stretch of beach with a moss-covered ledge running into it from the woods like a long gray wave. Julia sank down on it as if she had melted there. He lay down gratefully and put his head in her lap. Beyond a few feet from shore the Bay was veiled, and the sky above them was oyster-white and still. Julia did not look down at him but gazed ahead of her at the blurring water and stroked his forehead gently. Her face was tranquil. He closed his eyes. The stroking continued and it soothed him, but soon it became more vigorous and suddenly cold, as if her hands were icy. He started up with an exclamation.

Julia was standing over him, peering at him anxiously and dripping from the hindquarters down. A small wet hand was clamped on his forehead.

"I sat down in the water," she announced, "and got wet."

He stretched himself and could not resist a glance about him. He was on the familiar beach, and when he raised his eyes to the Bay the island was in its usual place. He ministered to Julia.

"What have you been doing?" he asked, grumbling a little.

"You were asleep, Daddy," she replied, "and I had to wake you up."

He said nothing and sat with his hands clasped around his knees, shaking his head to get it clear. Julia gazed at him thoughtfully and swung her arms back and forth. A glint came into her eyes and she fetched a sepulchral whisper.

"The island did come," she declared.

"Did it, now?" he said. "What did you do about it?"

Julia drew down the corners of her mouth and swung her body rapidly. When she spoke again she looked mischievous.

"I went there," she said, "and took you with me."

He leaned back and watched her.

"And then what happened?"

"I growed up," she declared, "and was big."

"Go on," he said, watching her intently, "anything else?"

"I get big every day," she told him, "at some time or other."

"That's fine," he said. "What did you have on today when you were big?"

But she seemed to have lost interest and scrambled off after a shoe that threatened to float out to sea. He pursued the subject, not very hopefully, when she returned.

"Try to tell me what you had on," he urged.

"When?"

"On the island when you were big."

She looked away.

"I don't bemember," she said.

"All right," he said, laughing and getting up. "Come along to supper or we'll be late."

She walked up the path ahead of him, her hair bouncing against her neck and her small bare feet padding down the pine-needles. All at once she stopped and faced him, her arms held up.

"You carry me, Daddy," she said.

He could see that she was tired, for the scimitar was softer and her mouth was relaxed and sweet. He grinned at her.

"Right, Mrs. 'Opkins," he said cheerfully. "Up you come."

He took her in his arms and strode along the path towards the house. Her eyes were big and vacant, and when he looked closely at them he thought that he could see a hint of violet in the clear blue. A thought struck him, and he leaned over and rubbed his cheek against hers. She suffered this indignity for a moment, then pushed his face away with one hand and looked up at him accusingly.

"Whiskers," she said.

Meals had margins around them in the summer. In winter the family fell into them as they would into a well, abruptly from whatever else they were doing, but on vacation meals wandered about after them or waited until they had gathered and had savored the idea of eating. When Ulen and Julia reached the house, steam and attractive smells were rising from the kitchen. He set her down at the door and steered her towards the bathroom. "Wash paws," he commanded. He stood behind her, turning on the tap and holding her small hands between his as he would a bunch of rose-leaves while he applied soap and melted the salt from them with his fingers. She regarded this procedure with composure and held out her hands with her stubby fingers extended to be dried. He mopped carefully, fearing to rub away the soft skin altogether.

"Horse," said Julia, when he had finished. Ulen got obediently to his knees and adjusted her on his back.

"Gallop," said Julia from above. Ulen galloped, amid disconnected squeals; twice around the table and into his stall, which happened to be the kitchen, to inquire whether supper was ready. It was, and he lowered Julia into her chair. They ate on the porch, and the Bay was a plate below them filling slowly with twilight. The darkness did not rush in from the east in these latitudes but settled imperceptibly from above, and only the shadow of the shoreline could be seen sliding eastward across the water and climbing up the islands, taking the cool copper light from them. At once they became dark green, but a high pink turret of cloud still rode above them. In the late summer the days were shorter and less reluctant to go, but even so they had to be wrung out; the wind went first and then the light, leaving at last a damp blue cloth of sky worn so threadbare that the stars shone through.

Severn had to be summoned. Ulen raised his voice to a bellow and directed it toward the Bay. He could see where the boy was, for when the shadow of the house lengthened and reached the low screen of birch trees that grew just above high-water mark, Severn's silhouette could be observed passing back and forth across the captain's walk on the top of the house. At the same time strange and mournful noises issued from him, for he was learning to play the clarinet. The captain's walk gave a full view of the Bay and the hills, and from the height they seemed at sunset to be sinking on fire out of sight. Severn used nature freely, but he seemed to feel no need to comment on it except through his instrument. Each fair evening just before supper he fled aloft and walked about or perched like Pan on the railing, his hair falling over his sharp eyes and his lips drawn tight around the clarinet, offering up his soul in various squeaks and groping themes of an appropriately reflective character. Ulen could see him nod his head in answer without moving the clarinet from his mouth; when he had finished the tune he was playing, he blew a few exaggerated notes and clattered down to supper.

Barbara floated to the table in a mist of romance. She had been reading, and her eyes were filled with angels, all of them male and very handsome. She looked out at the Bay as if she heard from the islands the tiny horns of the Prince Kalendar, and it was *Scheherazade* that she asked for after supper when Ulen went into the living-room to light the fire and begin the customary half an hour of recorded music. Neither she nor Severn was interested in hearing the ship go down against the rock with its warrior of brass, and Ulen turned to things of greater interest to Julia, for whom the period of music before bedtime was primarily intended. She sat and played with her dolls, having no way of saying what the music meant to her. When it was over she went upstairs with her mother, and Ulen followed a little later to hear her prayers.

These were not rigid and usually took the form of conversations. She lay on her back, her hands clasped and her eyes roving the ceiling for inspiration; she was expected only to sum up the day and make such observations as she would. Her voice was small and floated.

"God bless Mummy and Daddy and the telephone and my new white dress," she began tentatively. "I hope there will be another cake tomorrow." This did not seem to do, so she knitted her brows and took a fresh hold on the situation. "Across the ocean the bombs are spoiling all the gardens, so the children have no flowers and no vegebles. And their houses and their swings too. If I was there and they dropped a bomb, I'd just scurry home." There was a large and final sigh, and the end came in a rush. "If all the emenies loved all the other emenies there wouldn't be any emeniesamen."

Ulen stood for a moment and looked down at her. The telephone and your new white dress, he repeated inwardly, raising his eyebrows: you funny intent little thing. But she had gone soft and was asleep before he turned off the light.

One evening later in the season the Ulens drove to the station to meet Dr. Councill, whom they had persuaded to spend the last week of the summer with them. The night was still but crisp, and Ulen buttoned his leather jacket tightly under his chin. They brought an extra coat, for they knew that Councill would not bring one of his own from the heated city.

They reached the station in time to hear the train whistling hoarsely from the other side of the low ridge beyond the town that was railhead for the Bay. Being railhead made the traffic simpler than it was at a way station. There were never two-way crowds, for everyone who came to meet or board the two trains that ran daily in either direction was there for the same purpose. In a few moments the engine lumbered into view, its piston-rods moving slowly and its headlight thrust ahead of its boiler like a gaunt neck. It was drawing two cars and looked tired; it had started four hours before from the terminal a hundred miles away and was then heavily loaded, but it had shed mail and baggage and passengers on its way until it looked lean and hungry, and it ground to a stop just short of the bumper as if it were about to climb into bed.

It was a very tired rhinoceros that got out of the ancient carriage. Ulen threw the extra coat around him and took his bag. Councill brushed the cinders from his collar and looked up reverently at the train. "My God!" he said. "We stopped on a siding to wait for the down train and the conductor got out and picked a handful of raspberries. I know because I helped him."

They drove him home and fed him; once in his room he didn't re-appear for eighteen hours, and then they fed him again. When the meal was over he looked up with one of his rare grins. "Well, hello," he said. "I think I'm just coming to. It's nice to see you."

For a few days he did nothing but lie in the sun or sit in a corner of the porch and talk sparsely with Uncle Michael or watch the Bay. "Funny what it does to a man," he said, "to be able to look a long distance. Something happens to people who can't see very far."

After a day or two he shook off the top layers of heavy fatigue, and his eyes were less fixed when he came down to breakfast. He began noticing things around him that were less than ten miles off, and Ulen knew that he was ready to do the things he had come up for. Once they went fishing in the lake that lay inland beyond the arm of the mountain. It was still early when they reached it, and the lake was flat; no ripple moved the water against the forehead of ledge frowning above the deep water in front of the cabin that sheltered the family when they came on these expeditions. The surface was a plane of glass without a breath on it, and the mountain and the shoreline were so perfectly mirrored that Ulen's boat seemed to be floating inside a ring with sky above and below the narrow band of landscape. The only movement came from waterspiders, which darted about without making a ripple and bent the surface with their legs without breaking it. The quiet was complete, and when Ulen lowered the anchor over the bow its arms clanked loudly against the side. He let it drop slowly, watching it until it found bottom and toppled over with one claw sunk in the mud and the other pointed upward at him reproachfully. Several fish flashed darkly away from it.

They were in a little basin not far from shore where the water was about fifteen feet deep and cool. They impaled worms and settled themselves, Councill in the stern and

Ulen on the floorboards in the bow, his legs across the seat and his fishing hat tilted over his eyes. The little nests of worms could be seen clearly from the boat, dangling solitary and undisturbed a foot or two above the bottom. Ulen set fire to his pipe and watched the water. The flat calm could not last long, and even as he looked small fingers of air stole across the lake and frosted it; they reached in every direction, leaving pools still empty and unruffled, but in a few minutes these had gone and the whole lake was astir with a shred of wind too gentle to be felt inside the boat. It strengthened a little, and they could feel it like a veil drawn across their faces. Then the water wrinkled and mounted into tiny humps; from the shore came a lapping sound and the low waves wrote a watermark across the breasts of the rocks. With the wind came fish, and by lunch there was a comfortable meal for the household.

Afternoons they usually went sailing in the Bay, taking Mrs. Ulen or one of the children with them. For their last sail they all went, a little crowded in the small boat but each knowing where he belonged. Councill was taught to cast off the jib sheet when they came about and make it fast again on the other side after hauling the crackling canvas past the mast, and he did it with the slow strength of a man over sixty. The rest of the time he sat and snuffed the air, knowing nothing about sailing except to show confidence in the others who did.

They rowed out into the harbor, a little subdued because it was their last sail of the season. The boat was trim and lean, about thirty feet long and built light for speed, and it lay like a long wooden feather pulling gently at its mooring. They climbed aboard and began the ritual of making sail. The white canvas shot upwards and flapped, giving body suddenly to the small taut skeleton of hull and spars. Severn took the tiller and Ulen went forward to cast off, smiling to himself at the boy's quick competence. Severn studied the harbor. The black spar buoy inshore slanted toward them before a strong flood tide. The cluster of boats at anchor ahead of them had to yield a passage. The wind was fresh and steady from the southeast, but only at quarter force in the harbor; he could line up the red buoys close on the port hand and possibly make a clear run out of the harbor for Lismore Island, three miles away, without coming about. He nodded quickly to Ulen, who threw over the mooring line heavy with water and a green beard of weed. The boat fell off, feeling for the wind, and grew quiet when the sails curved outward into wings.

Severn held the sheet in one hand and the tiller in the other, walking her through the boats around them, and she slid by them, canted a little and rippling under her breath. Seeing an opening, he let out the sheet and veered into clear water; she straightened, with the wind over her quarter, and cut deeper. The ripple grew to a gurgle under her foot. He kept one eye on the pilings of the old wharf to port and the other on the near red buoy to starboard, to see how the tide was setting him, and when he thought it right he hauled the sheet close and headed upwind. She was tucked in now, slim and urgent, the red buoys in line and Lismore dead ahead. When she cleared the southern headland of the harbor the wind came at her full and deep, and she lay down under it, the weather rail curving overhand while the lee went down almost flush with the water and held there. Severn altered his course a bit, as though remembering, and headed straight for the far red buoy; when the tide set him down so that he passed it twenty or thirty feet to starboard he grinned through his flying screen of hair at Ulen, who drew down the corners of his mouth and nodded slowly.

Beyond the harbor the waves were higher and she began to throw water, crushing it sideways low and far to leeward and taking it in high flaunting ribbons that blew back from windward and arched over her foredeck. It crashed and hissed upwards with the sound of glass beads when her overhang fell upon it, but when it dropped again it was liquid and murmuring. Severn hauled the sheet a few inches closer until the boom was almost amidships, and pointed her nearer to the wind. She stiffened and bit deeper. He loved to make her fight her way, the tiller straining from him and every inch of her alive. He wanted to clear The Horns to windward and then reach over to the island. Her rail was under now and she was banging a little. Ulen looked at him and shook his head. He had let Julia come along for the special occasion, and she had to stay in the tiny cabin when they tacked. Seeing the floor at a forty degree angle was too much for her, and even with her mother and Barbara close by she was whimpering. Severn gave up reluctantly, his eyes on the waves breaking in a thin white collar over The Horns, and eased the sheet to reach for the island.

It was better this way and she jogged across the wind towards Seven Acre Ledge, just north of Lismore. It was mostly under water at high tide, but Severn knew its treacherous stretch to the south and allowed for it, making for the wide channel and the pool of deep water out of which the island rose like a pair of bent shoulders. Here he gave the tiller to Ulen and went forward to dangle his legs over the bow and watch the water flow under him.

Ulen paid close attention getting past the ledge and wearing around the end of the island. He didn't want to pass too close to it or it would take his wind away, and as it was the air suddenly grew light, as if a cloak had fallen on them. It was a beautiful island, but the shoreline was piled with high vindictive rocks loaded with driftwood on its seaward side. He watched it idly while the boat glided through its lee, and when the breeze freshened he hauled her close again and made up into the wind. Looking ahead, he saw for the first time that the horizon had changed. The air had shifted into the south, and where the sharp line of sky and water had been there was now a low white pillow laid on the ocean. He clucked to himself and calculated. The wind was fresh and steady, which meant that it was blowing in the fog. They wouldn't be becalmed in it, at any rate, but too much speed in a fog wasn't to his liking either. Probably four miles off. He had another ten or fifteen minutes to go towards it before he could clear the island and head for the harbor. Three miles across the Bay. To turn back the way they had come meant reaching across the wind. To go ahead around the island meant running home free; she did her best before the wind. He'd not be running straight before it, while the fog would be, but it was good enough. He'd put the genoa on her, not wanting to trust a spinnaker. Severn had cocked his head and was looking back at him. It would be close.

He called to Mrs. Ulen to take the tiller, got out the genoa, and with Severn's help struck the smaller jib. Mrs. Ulen luffed while they got the bigger jib up in its place, and then came about. Ulen returned aft and flattened the sails as close as he could. He was well up on the southern neck of the island and he hoped to skin by it as near as possible. Her rail was under again, but Julia would have to take it for a little while. If the tide had still been flooding he couldn't have made it, but it had turned and in a moment or two he saw the barrel-headed iron spindle that marked the end of shoal water off the island, and he cleared it with a little to spare. The fog was a mile to seaward of them and coming fast. Once past the spindle he slackened the sheets and brought the bow around until it pointed for the harbor. The boat seemed to take a deep breath, the boom lifting under the pull of the bagging mainsail, and pushed out a white carpet of water before her.

Ulen glanced at his pocket compass to fix his course in case. It wasn't very accurate but it would serve. The Wooden Plate Shoals, southeast of Lismore Island, were already a black smudge in the rolling fog, but on this course he saw that he would nearly hold his own. The boat veered and yawed when the waves overtook her from behind, and she would hang with her nose in the air until the wave rolled from under her and another caught her by the stern and pushed her hard into the trough, the water sizzling deck high from her shoulders. Hard to hold her on a course with such stuff behind her. It was a low fog, he saw, studying it, and it was patchy. If it ran ahead of him he might get in a clear space and be able to see the mountain above it. They were about even with The Horns and Lismore was blotted out. The fog was barely a quarter mile astern. Ulen caught his breath until he saw that it was only an arm reaching towards him; the main bank of it was farther away, and he altered his course slightly to escape it. Julia was peering from the cabin door. Seeing him look back at the fog, she looked too. Seeing him look again, she assumed that it was something to be concerned about and perhaps a little frightened. She put her thumb in her mouth.

"What is it, Daddy?" she asked.

"Fog," said Ulen.

"Is that bad?" she inquired.

"No," he replied absently, "it isn't. You can't see in it, that's all."

He thought that he might have said the wrong thing, for she gave a flutter of fear and gazed at him with wide eyes.

A few minutes later the edge of the forward arm swirled over the boat, damp and luscious. Ulen took a last look at the harbor when it faded into the driving white wool, and timed the yaws, trying to compensate and hold his course.

Julia had retreated into the cabin and was gazing out at him like a puppy. He could see her rolling her eyes about as if trying them. Then she came forward to the door and scrambled out.

"Is this the fog?" she asked in a stage whisper.

He nodded and grinned at her.

She grinned back happily. "I can see you," she said.

He beckoned to Severn to take over and picked her up in his arms.

"Well, that's all right then," he responded, holding her close to him. "I meant you can't see where the land has got to. It will clear soon. You watch."

She gazed at the water churning past them and lay slack against him, her soft face at ease again. All at once the fog lifted as quickly as it had come, and the mountain stood out sharp against the clear blue sky. The buoy was a few hundred yards away, and the wind, which had softened a little, had shifted into the southwest, blowing the fog away from them up the Bay.

Councill was looking at her with impassive affection. "Well," he said, "it's like waking up, isn't it?"

She looked at him with a little explosion of understanding.

"Is that how it is to be dead?" she asked suddenly. Her face had become inscrutable behind its firm young mask.

Ulen looked at her, puzzled. "We like to think that's how it is," he said, "but we don't really know." He laughed and set her down; then he went forward and stretched himself against the mast, tranquil again. The day began to glow with the gold of late afternoon. The waves were down and the breeze was a gentle push. Malay Island Light, at the entrance to the harbor, slipped by them, and the buoys were slanted seaward. The reefs beyond them growled lazily. Paul Snow was coming in from a trip after fresh bait, and they waved to each other. There was only half a sun above the tree line and it shrank until the tops of the pines were fired with it. The air was tipped with chill, and on the shore a branch of maple had turned into a wing of flaming red.

X

Datchett; Mr. Cameron and Mr. Burnside

JURY TRIALS would not begin until October, and the last part of September was scheduled for civil cases to be heard without a jury. Easier work in a way; a minimum of rulings on evidence and no charge. If objections were made, Ulen was inclined to listen to the evidence first and then invite a motion to strike it out, in order to be sure that he heard it. It was like the cow that stepped in the milk-pail; just try to strain it out. He believed that anything that a witness was determined enough to say in court had relevance; it was not always relevant to the case, but it was unfailingly relevant to the witness and the witness was necessarily relevant to the case. There were times, however, when he missed the presence of a jury keenly. They are a useful device to a judge for avoiding hard decisions, and they usually have the advantage of seeing a case in fuller colors, for lawyers cut their cases to the bone when trying before a judge only. Juries have the disadvantage, however, of being treated like children while the testimony is going on, but then of being doused with a kettleful of law during the charge that would make a third-year law student blanch.

More often than not Ulen could decide his non-jury cases readily, but at times he found himself faced by situations that could be resolved by no rational process whatever. They were insoluble, but he had the power and the duty to solve them somehow. Justice in such cases consisted in not hitting someone too hard, and the process of tempering the blow was nothing but the groping of a decent hunch. There was often no law in sight, and Ulen, glowering out of his window at the crowds below him in the street, wondered whether a decent instinct was enough. He had to know what men and women could take, and what he himself could take was not necessarily a universal criterion.

Jim Tobey entered and laid the pleadings on his desk. He had no time to read them, beyond noticing that they presented a personal injury case. They never said much in this type of action anyway, since the law automatically put in issue the circumstances of the accident and made it unnecessary for the defendant to file an answer unless a question of agency were involved. He saw that there was a short answer. Oh yes, there were two defendants; one worked for the other or he didn't, or else he had exceeded the authority of his employment. That was enough to know. There had been mail to dispose of and two or three lawyers to see before opening Court, and he liked to be prompt.

He found himself confronted by experienced counsel, who assumed that he had read the pleadings or didn't need to, and they set to work without preliminary statements. The plaintiff began by calling one of the defendants as under cross-examination. Ulen glanced again at the caption of the case: Peter Strong, a minor, by his next friend, Mathilda Wentz v. Harold Datchett and Michael Blewson. Hmm, must be one of those lonely accidents, if the plaintiff had to convict a defendant of negligence out of his own mouth. Or a fatal one.

Datchett approached the stand. He was about twenty-five and had wavy brown hair. Obviously trustworthy, Ulen thought as soon as he heard him speak; one of those who try earnestly to get along and who give out short, clear impressions without emotion. Datchett had the slightly crushed look of a man who knows a fact when he sees one. Ulen prepared himself to listen carefully. Neither the young man nor counsel would waste words, and he would get only an etching that he would have to amplify in his mind's eye. The simpler the facts the more difficult for him.

Datchett settled himself in the witness chair, informing the crier that he lived in the suburbs and was a truck-driver for Blewson, the other defendant. Counsel began to question him.

"Your wife was killed in this accident, was she not?"

"She was."

"Who is the minor plaintiff?"

"Her son."

"And yours?"

"No."

"How old were they when she died?"

"She was past twenty-one and he was four."

"How long had you been married?"

"Two months."

"Had she been married before?"
"No."
"Where is the boy?"
"He was always with her people."
"Did she support him?"
"Yes. She worked."
"Did you contribute anything to his support?"
"No. He just came to see us once or twice Sundays."
"How much did she pay?"
"She made fourteen dollars a week and gave her folks five for the boy."
"Who is Mathilda Wentz?"
"Her mother. Her old man died six months ago."
"Does she support Peter now?"
"I suppose so."
"You do not?" Datchett shrugged his shoulders, and counsel paused before going on.
"There was a Court order against his father for support, wasn't there?"
"Yes."
"Does he pay?"
"No. He left town and quit paying."
Counsel put his hands behind his head and leaned back. Then he looked over at Blewson's counsel as if by prearrangement. The other lawyer took up the questioning.
"You took your wife with you on this trip, didn't you?"
"I did."
"You saw Mr. Blewson before you left and asked his permission to take her?"
"I did."

"And he refused to give permission, did he not?"

"Yes."

"That's all."

Plaintiff's counsel arose.

"If Your Honor please, I should like to keep Mr. Blewson in the case because he's financially responsible, but I must admit that I have no other evidence than what Your Honor has just heard."

Ulen made an entry in his docket. "Very well," he said, "the Court finds in favor of the defendant Blewson. The case will proceed against the defendant Datchett only."

Blewson and his lawyer got up and left the courtroom. Counsel for the plaintiff continued.

"When did you start on this trip?"

"About six o'clock on Saturday evening, November second, last year."

"When did the accident happen?"

"Around ten o'clock the next morning."

"You drove all night?"

"Yes. We stopped once for a cup of coffee and once for an hour's sleep."

"How heavy was the truck?"

"Four tons empty. I had six tons of scrap iron on it."

"Where were you going?"

Datchett named a city in a neighboring State.

"Now tell us what happened."

Datchett leaned forward slightly, his elbows on the arms of the chair and his hands clasped.

"We got into the mountains about nine o'clock. I noticed the brake wasn't holding too good, so I planned to stop when we got to Cranston and get it fixed. There wasn't no other place without going all the way back to Coal City. It wasn't too bad and I got along all right until we got to Rose's Hill and started coming down. It's a long grade, not very steep at first, but the road gives a sharp right turn and then goes down fast. I saw a bus coming up behind me and it passed me on the easy grade where the road's straight. It's a two-lane highway. I was in third gear. Them trucks have five forwards. The bus got ahead and pulled over in front of me. I stayed about thirty feet behind it and we were coming to the turn, doing about twenty-five. Suddenly the bus slowed down real fast. I pushed the brake pedal but it went right down to the floor without catching. I had to act fast. The hill came right down to the road on my left and fell off steep on my right. I either had to ram the bus or go around it, so I threw the truck into high gear and stepped on the gas. I couldn't see around the curve until I got even with the bus. Then I seen a car parked half on the right side of the road and a big truck coming uphill around the curve about even with it. They were about a hundred feet ahead, and I must have been going thirty-five by then. I couldn't get over in front of the bus in time to miss the other truck and hit the parked car, and I couldn't slow down to get behind the bus again. I hit the truck head on. That's all I remember until I woke up in the hospital."

"How long were you laid up?"

"Six months. I broke both legs."

"Now, there's a sign at the top of Rose's Hill, isn't there, that says trucks must go into low gear when they come down?"

"Yes."

"And you were in third?"

"I was. I thought it was low enough."

"In spite of the fact that your brake wasn't working properly?"

"That's right. I meant to go into a lower gear when I hit the steep part."

"Did you sound your horn when you decided to pass the bus?"

"No. There wasn't time."

"That's all."

That was all, except for the bus driver and the one passenger who had seen anything. All they could say was that they had passed Datchett's truck and not long afterwards had to slow up because of the other truck and the parked car. Then Datchett passed them rapidly and the accident happened almost at once. After Datchett's truck hit the other one it bounced and went partly through the fence. They got him and his wife and the driver of the other truck into the bus and took them to the nearest hospital, ten miles farther on, but she was dead on arrival. Counsel told Ulen at side-bar [1] that

---

[1] This was a bar, or rail, in Westminster Hall where lawyers came to take certain rules that were uncontested and could be granted as a matter of course. This is now done at the regular bar that separates the bench from the rest of the courtroom. A side-bar conference, however, takes place within this august space when the lawyers want to speak privately to the judge, or vice versa. They must make their way through a maze of desks, chairs, and stenographers' apparatus until they are in position to rest their chins on the edge of the bench itself and deliver themselves uncomfortably of messages beginning: "Your Honor." If the judge begins, it is usually: "Say, Jim, what do you think you're trying to do?" The jury, when there is one, always looks suspicious, as it should. At times such conferences are necessary, as when I once had to inform a lawyer that his fly was open and could think of no other way of doing it.

the driver of the other truck had also died, and that Datchett had been tried for manslaughter but had been acquitted of criminal negligence. Mrs. Datchett's mother testified also, but there was little that she could add. Her husband had always had a weak heart and of course he could get no insurance. His earning power was limited too, but they had managed; now that he was gone, she could do sewing and washing and perhaps she could get along. She was none too well herself. Boys need lots of things. Datchett picked his teeth with a match and looked at the floor while she was testifying.

There was no defense to present. The case was over. Having laid the bleak problem in Ulen's lap, they all sat and watched him stolidly. He waited a minute, hoping there might be more, but no one moved and he got up with a little shake of his head.

"I'll take it under advisement, gentlemen," he said. "I can't possibly decide it now."

He returned to his chambers and flung himself into his chair. Why on earth had they agreed to try a thing like that without a jury? He wondered if it was because a jury might disagree and they knew that he had to make a decision of some sort. So he had to be a jury, did he? He didn't always agree with the verdicts that juries brought in; he thought he could see more clearly and sharply, because of his training, but that wasn't the answer. The community had the right to be wrong. No, that wasn't it either. The community had the right to try to be accurate, and most likely it was better so. There ought to be a brighter class of people on juries, he said to himself, kicking his desk in sudden anger at the community for not providing them. The legislature ought to do something. He ought to do something to make the legislature do something. He kept kicking the desk. Getting off the track a bit. Well, a jury could easily find that Datchett had been negligent; coming down a hill with ten tons moving under him and disregarding the sign about low gear when he knew that his brakes were poor. He had probably done what any reasonable man would have done when the emergency was upon him, but he had created the emergency. Seemed a pity to enter a verdict against a young man like that; he'd been through a lot himself and he had no insurance to cover him. Two broken legs, a dead wife, a criminal trial, and a suit for damages was a great deal to take. And he had told the truth, although it hurt him. Funny to find that fact even remarkable, but it was. Anything he'd have to pay must come out of his salary as he earned it, and the verdict would have to be for a substantial amount. Ulen knew that he could control the execution of the judgment [2] that would be entered on the verdict; no rushing in and arresting Datchett on a capias [3] for not paying it all at once.

Why was he fussing so over it? After all, Datchett had married the girl, knowing about Peter. The way things were now with his wife's mother, he would probably have had to take

[2] The judgment is not hanged or electrocuted. It is collected. The sheriff goes out and takes what he can find that belongs to the person against whom the judgment has been entered, and only the debtor's clothes, salary, schoolbooks, and Bible are exempt.

[3] Originally a Court writ telling the sheriff to take someone into custody for not obeying a Court order. Now used to arrest people in civil actions for delinquent taxes, for injuries by violence, for fraud, and the like. But it is a civil arrest and must be used carefully. There are other capias writs, all in Latin; capias ad audiendum judicium, ad computandum, ad faciendum, ad respondendum, ad satisfaciendum, in withernam, pro fine, and utlagatum — but never mind.

the boy in by this time and support him outright, even if there hadn't been an accident. The girl must have been pretty decent, not forcing it on him from the start. He'd killed her by his carelessness and he'd have to take the consequences, even though the child wasn't his own. Sure, a jury'd find him negligent every time and shrug their shoulders. A verdict against him was the equivalent of making him support the kid. Gosh, Ulen thought, turning his chair and stretching his legs straight out, none of this is very judicial; most of it's outside the record, but it's what a jury would probably do. Not much room for exquisite justice. His mind snapped shut. All right, verdict for the plaintiff. That was clear enough.

But for how much? He gave a grunt as an idea struck him, and he went out quickly into the corridor. Datchett and his lawyer had stayed behind for a little while and were now walking slowly away, talking together. Ulen called to them and they stopped.

"By the way," he said, addressing Datchett, "do you happen to have a picture of your wife?"

The young man produced a worn photograph from his wallet. Ulen looked at it. A dull round face looked back at him, the head a little on one side and the eyes listless. Born to be a passenger, Ulen thought; she would probably extend a limp hand to be shaken, and in a few years even the faint smudge of prettiness would be gone. He handed back the picture with thanks and returned to his room. So. Five dollars a week and a photograph was all that he had to go on. The legal measure of damages was the economic value of the girl's life to her son during his minority. He got out his pencil and started to figure what it would be at the worst.

Seventeen years. Eight hundred and eighty-four weeks at five dollars a week. About forty-four hundred dollars. Reduce it to its present worth, so that, if invested, it would be no greater at the end of the period than the total of wages paid weekly would have been. Silly to do that, even though it was the law. Datchett couldn't pay it at once, or even half of it; he'd have to pay it week by week. But the judgment would be for a lump sum and interest would accumulate on it. That would make the calculation easier, but not the rest of it.

It was sheer necromancy. What was the economic value of a life? Had she lived, the girl might not have supported the boy at all, wanting to make a fresh start and forget him; or the boy might become a prodigy at something and could have supported her. Life in seventeen years might do a thousand things to them both that could increase or extinguish her economic value to him. Five dollars a week would not be enough when he was older. But the law stood at Ulen's back, wringing its hands and pointing its finger at the evidence, such as it was. The economic value of a vanished life, it demanded of him, in dollars and cents, from five dollars a week and a photograph. But it gave him a little more, when he stopped to think of it. These were average people with average lives and points of view, and the law was built upon average behavior. The unseen presence behind him seemed brighter at the idea; easier than it looked, perhaps. But the hitch was that people usually didn't know that they were average and had little obstinate ambitions to be more. That too had to be allowed for. Ulen threw back his head and rubbed his eyes hard with the heel of his palms. He'd have to find the answer somehow. Later. It would have to rest for a while now. And although he knew that he'd study it, he also knew that in the end he would award something near two thousand or twenty-five hundred dollars.

Jim Tobey entered and handed him some more pleadings. "Next case," he said, laconically, "also non-jury."

Mr. Dyner had come from one of the more sober of the Slavic countries and was a very plain man. He was tall and appeared to have great dignity, but when seen close at hand it became obvious that he was simply wary and a little stiff. He was also a man of few words, and they too were plain and realistic. He worked as a carpenter for whoever needed one, and when he was paid he put the money in his pocket and said: "Thank you," but he kept no records of his earnings. If he had ever heard of the growing need of sharing his financial secrets with the government, he did not let on, and it is likely that he would have heard of it from his landlady, Mrs. Durkin, who talked too much and was a widow; but she was impressed by his unconscious stateliness and held her tongue. He made about thirty dollars a week and paid his rent promptly.

His room was on the third floor front, just under the roof. The house was very old and almost slatternly, and his room was so small that it could not have been that size originally but must have shrunk with age. A stovepipe, which had long since been out of use, had been disconnected at the ceiling and a round plug inserted in its gaping mouth to keep the cold air out and the hot air in. This was directly over Mr. Dyner's bed. The rest of the pipe, about six feet long, rose through the roof and was covered on the outside with thick tar paper. Over its open top there was a wooden cover held down by two or three bricks.

Mr. Dyner went to bed at a moderate hour one Sunday evening and was not awakened early next morning either by the sound of workmen climbing over the roof above him or by the first tentative blows that they struck upon it. A minute later, however, he was jarred awake by a heavy thump on his back and when he found himself unable to move he tried to call out for help, but a severe pain in his ribs prevented him. Twisting his head painfully, he saw a length of pipe lying partly across his body and a good deal of dirt on his bed. He couldn't see it very clearly, for the blinds were drawn and the room was dark. Half an hour afterwards he was able to crawl from under the covers and go for help. When the doctor came, Mr. Dyner was found to have two broken ribs and a sprained back, and these injuries kept him from work for about eight weeks.

The noise above him had resumed, and he discovered with difficulty a few days later from Mrs. Durkin, who had suddenly become reluctant to talk, that a Mr. Plank and his helper had arrived that morning to fix the roof, which was made of slate and was shedding its teeth. That was all she would say. Mr. Plank's version of the affair, given to Mrs. Durkin unguardedly when she told him that Mr. Dyner had been hurt, was not complicated. He knew about roofing and had seen at once that the slate had to be removed by using a heavy spade-like instrument that he carried with him. Mr. Plank had come from another of the Slavic countries but did not share Mr. Dyner's taciturnity. He described the situation to Mrs. Durkin with considerable color. Around the pipe was a good place to begin, he thought, since the pieces of slate there were of small and irregular shapes in order to fit as closely as possible. Mr. Plank aimed one or two blows at the base of the pipe, whereupon it gave a plop and disappeared. He peered through the hole as well as he could from his position on the ladder, but he could not see very well and assumed that the pipe had fallen into the attic. He sent his helper for a sheet of tin, and when it arrived he fastened it over the hole and went on working.

When Mr. Dyner was able to get around again, he paid his rent without saying anything and moved, taking the pipe with him. About a week later Mrs. Durkin and Mr. Plank were served with papers alleging that Mr. Dyner had been rendered sick, sore, lame, and disordered, and asking five thousand dollars in damages. Mrs. Durkin went Oh! and put her hand on her mouth. "You never can tell," she said in conclusion to the group at supper, "about them people in which they don't ever say nothing."

When Ulen returned to the courtroom, the pipe was on the rail in front of the counsel tables, at which two young men were sitting. He recognized them as lawyers whom he had admitted to practice a month or two before. He chuckled to himself, thinking back. They sat with the air of tense but nonchalant dismay that he remembered, still with a twinge of torture, from the first case that he had ever tried. His opponent, to add to his panic, had been a seasoned member of the bar who had been unfortunate enough to be unable to locate his client for trial but had decided to go on anyway; it was a very small case and he thought that he could amuse himself by kicking up some dust. To complete the picture, the case had been listed for jury trial before a new judge named Parkinson, and it was his first case too. It involved a contract, and a sharp eye was needed to see the simple but veiled question at issue. By the end of the trial the three men each had a theory of his own, but the theories somehow failed to mesh; the dust kicked up by Ulen's redoubtable opponent had enveloped everybody. The jury, puzzled but determined, had indicated by their verdict their conviction that no one would bother going to law unless he had a case, a view that had doubtless been strengthened by the failure of the defendant to appear. Ulen had arisen in a rosy glow of triumph, and his adversary, his eyes twinkling just enough to go unnoticed, had shaken hands with him warmly. The first case is a matter of more than temporary moment, and it has its traditions.

Ulen braced himself for the impact. Pity they were both in this position; one of them had to lose. Mr. Cameron represented Dyner. Mr. Burnside represented Mrs. Durkin and Plank. Although Ulen had taken time to read the pleadings and knew the outlines of the case, Mr. Cameron arose and fortified him still further with an involved description of it, during which Mr. Burnside interrupted with an objection to the effect that Mr. Cameron was arguing his case instead of stating it. Counsel's opening statement, he declared, was not the time to argue. Ulen nodded pleasantly. Mr. Cameron had trouble getting on the track again but seemed determined not to show it. There was a moment's silence while he recovered.

"I press my objection," said Mr. Burnside.

"Well, now," Ulen remarked, "since there isn't any jury but me, you can both go ahead pretty much as you please. Formalities can be at a minimum. I'll see to it that the jury isn't misinformed." He beamed at them.

"Exception," said Mr. Burnside. Ulen bowed slightly.

Mr. Burnside looked at him anxiously. "Does Your Honor grant my exception?" he asked.

"Oh, indeed I do," Ulen answered.

This happened three more times before Mr. Cameron appeared to be stifled by the situation and sat down abruptly in the middle of a sentence. He motioned to Dyner to take the stand.

Neither Dyner nor Ulen had a very easy time of it from then on. The young lawyers quickly lost sight of the case in their effort to see to it that neither of them put anything over on the other. Mr. Cameron studied each question in order to make it unassailable, a procedure that appeared to be facilitated if the question were cast in impressive language. Mr. Burnside seemed to feel that he would be dishonored if Mr. Cameron could think up a question that had nothing wrong with it. After half an hour of this the pipe had not yet fallen on Mr. Dyner's back. He began looking at Ulen as if in doubt that he was in the right courtroom. Finally Mr. Cameron drew a long breath and plunged in.

"What – er – what function were you performing at about eight a.m. in the morning of March 26 of this year?"

"What?" said Dyner.

"Objected to," said Mr. Burnside.

"Why?" inquired Mr. Cameron.

"It assumes that there was a function and that the witness was performing it," Mr. Burnside replied. "Therefore it is leading."

"He may answer," Ulen ruled, granting Mr. Burnside an exception, "if he can."

"Answer," said Mr. Cameron.

"Answer what?" Dyner asked.

"The stenographer will please read the question," Mr. Cameron murmured. The stenographer rustled for a moment and then repeated.

"Don't understand them words," Dyner muttered.

"I move that the question be stricken out," Mr. Burnside said, arising triumphantly.

"Objected to," said Mr. Cameron. "Your Honor overruled my learned opponent's objection to it."

"The witness does not understand the question," Mr. Burnside insisted.

"I object to my learned opponent saying what the witness does or does not understand," Mr. Cameron announced. "However, I shall withdraw the question."

"Objected to," said Mr. Burnside, "until my motion has been ruled upon."

Ulen scratched his head a trifle too hard. "I overrule the motion to strike; also the objection to the motion to strike; also the objection to counsel's statement of the witness's understanding; and also the objection to the withdrawal of the question. Exceptions in all directions. Now look here," he concluded, turning to the witness, "tell me what you were doing that morning."

"I sleep," Dyner replied.

Mr. Burnside arose decisively.

"I object to any further testimony from this witness," he said.

But Dyner had lost patience. He suddenly leaped to his feet with wide gestures.

"You no object to nothing," he shouted. "I object. I sleep. Pipe fall from roof on my back. Break two ribs. I can do no more. I object to that. You object to nothing. What for a business goes on here, Judge?" he demanded, sitting down slowly and looking wrathfully at Ulen.

Mr. Burnside persisted.

"The witness admits he was asleep, Your Honor," he said. "He is incompetent to tell what happened."

"I tell what happen," Dyner broke in, getting up again. "Pipe not there when I go to bed. Pipe on top of bed when I wake up. On top of me too. Pipe there now." He pointed at it with an angry finger. "My ribs busted here." He clasped his sides. "What more you want? You pay me money what Judge say is right and shut up." He subsided, trembling.

Mr. Burnside shot to his feet.

"I move for the withdrawal of a juror," he said excitedly.

"There aren't any," Ulen replied, "and I decline to withdraw myself. After all, counsel, a litigant has the right to state his case, and Mr. Dyner has just done so with considerable precision. What happened to his ribs must of course await the doctor. Don't forget that you may cross-examine."

Mr. Burnside had apparently forgotten that he could and sat down, somewhat mollified, after having carefully taken another exception.

After that, Ulen got down to business and held them in line. He couldn't let Dyner think what he obviously was thinking about court procedure, and the trial got along faster.

They ran into some difficulty later over the proof of Dyner's earnings, because of his lack of records, and Mr. Burnside interrupted, over Mr. Cameron's vigorous objection, to ask Dyner whether he had filed an income tax return.

Dyner spread large palms. "What is this?" he asked.

"Government paper," Mr. Burnside said, loudly and distinctly. "Did you tell the government what money you made?"

Dyner's shoulders rose to his ears and he turned towards the bench.

"Why I tell government what money I make?" he inquired. "Make thirty dollars every week, pay ten dollars rent regular, rest of money go in pocket to live. Whose business is this?"

"Whose indeed?" Ulen observed.

Mr. Burnside arose with the air of acknowledging victory after a hard fight.

"I now move for a verdict for defendants," he announced. "A man who violates the law may not recover. Sixty-one State Reports, one-seventy."

"Oh, yes, he can," Ulen observed soothingly, "sixty-one State Reports to the contrary notwithstanding."

Mr. Burnside looked horrified.

"But Your Honor! He admits that he filed no income tax return."

"Well, never mind," Ulen went on, "I sha'n't tell on him. It goes only to his credibility here. Exception. Let's proceed, please."

They proceeded to the doctor. Mr. Cameron's first hurdle

was to qualify [4] him, which he did very thoroughly. By the time he had finished, the doctor stood out as a person of incredible learning and experience; he appeared to have caught the spirit of the thing and was doing nicely. He had undergone an unusually extensive training, including study abroad, and not only was he on the staff of the best hospitals, whose specialities Mr. Cameron urged him to describe at length, but he belonged to a great number of learned societies for which he had written papers on various abstruse medical subjects. He summarized these colorfully and allowed himself to be drawn slowly through his entire career. Mr. Cameron felt at length that the doctor was sufficiently qualified to diagnose a pair of broken ribs and a sprained back. Mr. Burnside, however, took the opposite view. The doctor looked pained. After a barrage of objections, the doctor was permitted to answer this question: "What was the condition, if any, of the plaintiff's posterior?"

"In the ordinary meaning of posterior," the doctor said seriously, "it was normal."

Ulen gave him a reproachful look and turned to fend off Mr. Burnside, who was moving to strike out all of the doctor's testimony, to non-suit the plaintiff,[5] and to change the

[4] Witnesses must state facts, not opinions, and they must never guess. An exception to this dubious rule is the case of the expert witness. His professional opinion, based upon his special learning and experience, is of course valuable because it is often the only possible evidence of a fact. Such an opinion is a guess in evening clothes and is permissible if the expert's training is shown in order to enable the judge and jury to determine how expert he is and consequently to evaluate his testimony.

[5] On defendant's motion at the end of the plaintiff's case, the judge may rule that the plaintiff has shown no legal basis for his suit and stop the trial. This is not as final as a verdict, for if the Statute of Limitations hasn't run out, the plaintiff may start a new suit and supply the defect in his old case, if he

venue.[6] To add to his difficulties, Mr. Cameron was growing sulky.

"I ask leave to try my case in my own way," he pleaded, getting up. "The plaintiff was injured, and I – "

"Objected to," shouted Mr. Burnside. "My learned opponent will try his case according to the rules of evidence. I object to speeches."

"I wasn't speaking. I was addressing the Court."

"You were. In seventy-eight – "

But the doctor was getting impatient.

"This man had two broken ribs and a sprained back," he asserted, looking at his watch.

Mr. Burnside was on his feet with a howl of anguish, but Ulen took hold again and directed Mr. Cameron to proceed. He did so by producing an immense hypothetical[7] question which he had prepared in advance and which he now started to read. Mr. Burnside seized a pencil and began listing his objections. Ulen cut them short.

"Granted a pipe fell on him," he said to the doctor, "would it have caused these injuries?"

---

can. A verdict against him, unappealed from or affirmed on appeal, would finish him finally. Defendants, for that reason, usually refrain from putting on a defense and ask for a directed verdict in their favor as a matter of law. Young defense lawyers try for non-suits – they look like sharp and sudden victories, but often they're not.

[6] To transfer a case to another judicial district in order to avoid local prejudice or excitement and secure a fairer trial.

[7] A device for bringing an expert witness up to date on the case and giving him a basis on which to express an opinion. He will not be allowed to do so unless he has all of the pertinent facts before him, and very often he has been called in just before trial, without knowing a thing about the case of his own knowledge. His wide experience in the type of situation involved in the case may be of great benefit.

"Yes," said the doctor at once.

Mr. Burnside's agony was apparent.

"If Your Honor please," he began, as if expelling a bad oyster, "I must respectfully object — "

"You may object respectfully or disrespectfully," Ulen returned a bit tartly. "I'm past caring. But we must get this trial finished. Overruled."

When the plaintiff finally rested his case and the defense went on, Mr. Cameron tried to repay Mr. Burnside in kind, but he had little opportunity, for Mrs. Durkin took command and talked them both down, and Ulen too. He tried to keep her in check, but she simply looked through him and raised her voice a little without pausing. He had to let her go; when he raised his voice she raised hers higher. She had on a hat of artificial flowers that was fastened only at the back, and it bobbed up and down with the emphasis of her speech, which appeared as regularly as the ridges of a washboard and sounded like one. She had an enlarged view of relevancy, and the three men sat looking crushed while she flowed from subject to subject like an oil fire, but she gave Ulen all he needed. She told him that she had bought the house only a month before Mr. Dyner moved in and that she had tested the pipe by standing on a stepladder, which she described in detail; the pipe had seemed very firm and secure. She also related Plank's version of what had happened, and laid emphasis on it; she seemed to know the consequences of being an independent contractor,[8] and she got along very well with-

[8] Nice for a defendant to have one about if possible. If you have one to build your house, he will be liable and you won't be when one of his workmen drops a brick on somebody's head. This won't follow if you insist on telling him what to do and how to do it.

out benefit of questions. When she had finished at last, both lawyers arose mournfully and moved to dismiss the case for a new hearing later. The situation seemed to have conquered them, and the notes of their prepared questions lay in little heaps. Ulen regarded them for a moment with mixed feelings.

"No," he said. "This mustn't happen again. The only thing that requires a new trial is you yourselves. While you've been setting off the rules of evidence as if they were a lot of sky-rockets, the case has been rolling along very nicely. Cases will do that every time, and with experience you'll come to see that in the long run they will try you instead of your trying them."

The lawyers started to pack up their brief cases.

"I think you've forgotten something," Ulen observed. "Mr. Plank."

They sat down sheepishly, the fight out of them. Ulen grinned at them and they grinned back.

Mr. Plank was disposed of briefly.

"I do nothing," he said in response to Ulen's question, holding his hands stiffly before him, palms outward, as if his story had a weight that had to be held up. "I climb up the ladder. I look at the pipe. I say to myself: 'Plank,' I say, 'Plank, you must be very, very careful of that pipe and not to touch it or you hurt somebody very bad.' So I am very, very careful. You see, Judge," he went on, putting the fingers of one hand against his chest, "I know my business very good, see? I know if things fall down on people, Plank's business fold up. So I just look at that pipe and do not touch. I have the ladder here, so, and the pipe is there, so. I do nothing, nothing at all, but look at that pipe. All of a sudden that pipe give a little wiggle, like that, it make a little noise like a scratch – hrrrch – like that, and all at once it go down, out of sight, like that. All I know. I kiss the Bible."

Plank kissed the Bible, arising abruptly and clamping his lips upon it. Then he seated himself again and grasped the arms of the witness chair as if he were shaking hands with them.

Ulen observed him affably.

"I don't believe a word of it," he remarked. "Start all over again from the beginning and tell me the truth."

Plank appeared to be prepared for this reaction.

"Judge, I tell now the truth," he said, spreading all of his fingers and gazing at them lugubriously. "I swear. I kiss the Bible.

"Judge, I feel very sick that morning. My stomach, it is bad, very, very bad. Nothing sits on it. Maybe I lean a little too heavy on my tool near the pipe, I do not know. But I do not hit the pipe, ohhhh no. I know my business, but my stomach – pfui! Now is the truth. I speak no more."

Ulen arched his eyebrows.

"Well," he said, "speak just enough to tell me what you said to Mrs. Durkin about the pipe."

Plank drew himself up with great dignity and spread his hands.

"What can I say, Judge? It is so with a woman. When the man dies, the woman is kaput. I work hard for her, very, very hard. I fix the roof. I ask for pay. Nothing happens, nothing. So what can I say? I speak no more."

Ulen glanced at Mrs. Durkin, who opened her mouth very wide and left it that way. He reached for his docket. Easy enough to decide the case on the spot, the facts being what they were, and Mr. Burnside did not have to go down to utter defeat after all.

"Just a minute, gentlemen," he said, and wrote. The young lawyers stood as if awaiting execution. Ulen raised his head and looked at them.

"The Court finds in favor of the plaintiff," he announced, "but against the defendant Plank only. The Court finds in favor of the defendant Durkin. Damages are assessed in the sum of seven hundred and fifty dollars."

Mr. Burnside appealed and wrote a portentous brief, but the appellate court disposed of it in a few lines, per curiam.[9] It was a case of no importance and was never cited in later decisions.

---

[9] "By the Court." An opinion is sometimes signed this way instead of by the judge who writes it when the case is either trivial or of tremendous importance, or when the Court issuing it wants to make it particularly clear that the decision represents the Court's policy. I regret to say that in cases of a political nature involving intense public interest, individual judges often acquire a passion for anonymity.

XI

Professor Alberson

A JUDGE'S DAY in chambers is not always the jewel of seclusion it is supposed to be, nor is his chambers necessarily a place of learned peace. The day had begun badly for Ulen, even on the train. He thought that he was well hidden behind his paper, but Mrs. Hastings was on the lookout for a pair of ears, willing or unwilling, and she had become an expert in surmounting the barrier of the daily news. She peered unashamedly, and if she saw what she wanted and the seat was vacant, she sat down. Ulen, feeling the cushion sag beneath substantial female pressure on his left, glanced up and was lost.

Mrs. Hastings's eyes popped a little and maintained an even stare above whatever stream of conversation she was putting forth. Judged from the look on her face, everything she said was of the same importance, which to most of the people with whom she talked was little or nothing. She enjoyed her own talk because it presented an impenetrable wall against her listeners' difficult subjects, and she found it necessary to talk in order to prevent difficult subjects from arising in her own mind and bothering her. Glancing around the car, Ulen saw a few relieved and sympathetic glances.

Mrs. Hastings poured forth a spray of conversational bird-shot. Ulen made a show of listening, nodding regularly and resting his eyes not too absently on the newspaper now lying on his lap, the important news upward. He might have weathered the ride without too much distraction, had he not heard Mrs. Hastings calling attention to the rows of new houses on the outskirts of the city. He looked out idly at them; they were neat and had offsets here and there, to prevent the customary monotony of that kind of building. Between the rows there were gay little backyards, some of them set out in flowers and a good many tailored more soberly with vegetables. A few colored children were playing contentedly in the wide, newly paved streets. Problem, Mrs. Hastings was saying while she looked at them, her voice lowered ominously; a real Problem. Springing up everywhere, these houses, and cluttering the landscape. That used to be old Mrs. Hartley's fine estate, and now look at it, just look at it. She felt a difficult subject rising, but having started it she had to put it down. Well, she concluded, we let them into the country; she supposed we had to do something for them.

Ulen turned a baffled eye upon her and grew even more uncommunicative. At the terminal she found another friend and dropped him unceremoniously, and he trudged gloomily to the courthouse. His mail was scanty, as usual, although it contained two requests to make speeches on subjects wholly unconnected with the law, which he curtly directed his secretary to decline, and a request from a new organization called World Purposes to evaluate its program. The letter proceeded crisply to outline what World Purposes were. They included every known area of human endeavor and were to be "synchronized by the articulation of current thought on the part of those to whom the enumerated fields present particular significance." He ran his eye glumly down the long list of directors, honorary and actual, and of advisors and member organizations. Yes, there was old Judge Parkinson, lending his name. The Assistant Secretary who had signed the letter, humbly, by the president per herself, was a friend of his. He picked up a pencil and scribbled in the margin: "Omissions – the Golden Rule By Act of Congress, Present Implications of Magna Carta, Modern Trends in Beetle Culture, and the Epithalamiums (if any) of Pliny the Elder. I bleed but cannot synchronize." He drew a line under his friend's name and growled at Miss Dingle to mail it back to her. "Better mark it personal," he added. "Since she's the only one who does any work over there, she'll understand."

Interruptions fell upon his day like a series of summer showers. He had an opinion to work out, but the ideas that he had been gathering grew tired of diving under the numerous waves of invading words and personalities. Two lawyers, followed by the court clerk, sought an audience. The clerk handed to Ulen the papers in their case and withdrew. They had come to fix a time for hearing, they said, but within a minute they had forgotten Ulen and were rummaging in their files, shouting and refuting each other. Ulen gathered that it was an equity suit, something about an old woman and setting aside a deed. He remembered that the older lawyer had come to see him about it the other day. He reminded them that they hadn't begun the hearing yet, and fixed the next day for it; he'd study the papers, he said, and be ready for them. They grinned sheepishly and retired, excusing themselves for bothering him. He got paid by the State for being bothered, he said, and peered at them over his glasses, smiling a little belatedly.

He threw the papers aside, and it was not until afternoon that he was able to take them up again and look at them. He was weary from having his train of thought driven underground and his attention shot at and wrestled with, and he unfolded the pleadings with the feeling that each page weighed a ton. Alberson v. Porter. Didn't look very complicated: a bill in equity [1] and a little testimony of some kind. He kinked the creases in the middle to keep the pages flat and began to read.

Professor Alberson sat in front of his fire and looked at it. He had looked at it so often that he wondered why he hadn't

---

[1] Originally in England, litigants had to carry their complaints to the king at the seat of government. As business increased, judges were sent out into the districts, but the habit of going to the king persisted, and the king referred such cases to his Chancellor. This right to apply direct to the king became a welcome method of getting around the harsh narrowness of the Common Law, which often denied a remedy for undoubted injuries either by not having provided any or by requiring unreasonable technicalities in presentation and proof. Equity cases are still carried separately in court records and are resorted to for quick relief with a minimum of technical fuss. They are begun by filing in Court a "bill." They include such things as divorce, probate, injunctions, accounting, certain clouds on title to real estate, and fraud of one kind or another. Juries can be had on request but are generally not used in equity, and within reasonable limits the judge's conscience controls. In many places he is still called Chancellor when he hears equity cases.

tired of it long ago. He had tired of almost everything else; it was odd how interests slid away, one or two at first, then a handful, and at last everything but a few cores to which he had attached his life so firmly and so long ago that he guessed they would have to shake themselves free from him before he could die. Looking at the fire had remained, most likely because it gave something besides warmth alone, a kind of fluid thaw that melted the stiffness in him and in a quiet way turned back the years a little. His legs, stuck out on the bench before him, felt like sluices down which the wakefulness was running out of him; he seemed to be pouring into sleep. He knew he wasn't, for he was on to that old trick by now. The blanket of sleep had worn very thin and came grudgingly. He was simply dripping away altogether, and he knew it, and it didn't matter.

The world had narrowed about him so unmistakably that when he sat like this it consisted only of the fire in the grate, so familiar to him that he knew every crack and chip in the blackened bricks. Late at night the fire grew old too and sang a little in the wood. Strange, how inanimate things seemed to be at their best when they were old, and in humankind it was usually the other way. He was well over eighty himself and had forgotten almost all he ever knew, and that didn't matter either. He could remember very far back quite clearly; that was pleasant, and he spent his days in those old places, recalling how he used to say, when his memory was really good, that he could remember before he was born, being afraid that he would be a girl. Not such a laughing matter now. Some of those old Tibetan monks had spent years, as immobile as he was now, trying to think back through birth into earlier incarnations, and some of them believed that they had succeeded. Perhaps they had; maybe this backward urge of the mind at the end of life meant something.

Security had remained too. In fact, it had grown under the huge pile of years, the only thing that had. Sixty-one years in this house, he and Alice, the only home they had ever had together. It was a mite too large for them, but who could have told from her blushes and the extra white shine of her eyes when they bought it, a mite too large then also, that she would not have any children? There had always been a room or two in it that hadn't grown up with the rest of the house but had remained young and unused, with more dust in them to hide the dead remnants of expectancy than in the others. Many of his books were stored there now, and the rooms were chill and austere, as if they had been deeply hurt long ago. To make matters worse, the books were in a dreadful mess; he knew where everything was and could lay his hands instantly upon what he wanted, only he hadn't wanted to for a long time, and the piles of books and pamphlets and unfinished treatises had sunk into despondency too and were disappearing beneath a dust that was less dust than the drifting shale of time.

Even these discarded rooms played their part in the feeling of security that the house had thrown like an extra skin about him and Alice. Only after years does the full sense of possession come and a house becomes a home; then that fades away and the place becomes a garment, trustworthy enough to be taken wholly for granted and to give security so secure as never needing to be thought of. A man stepped into it at night as he stepped into his shoes in the morning, and when it came time for him not to work any more he stepped into it once and for all and never took it off again. Only when he paid his taxes did there come to him the vaguely disturbing realization, like a faint groundswell raising him slightly, that there was a power in the outer world capable of threatening his security; but he had always been able to pay his taxes, and even that realization had faded to a mere irritation at having to do something, once a year, on time.

And Alice had remained. He did not need to lift his eyes from the fire to see her exact position in her chair, and he could tell from the sound of her knitting needles what was going on in her, even where she was in her row: at the beginning the needles were dogged, as if thinking of the distance ahead; sober and dependable in the middle; and a bit quickened and careless near the end. When there was no sound she was nodding, making short gentle rushes at sleep like a kitten with a ball, and the gleaming needles lay still in her lap, the bright steel a strange weapon in the wasted hands with their blue veins mounted in ridges on them. The needles had been quiet longer than usual this evening, and he turned his eyes to her. She was not dozing but was staring vacantly at a point just above the fire, and one lock of white hair had fallen over her eyes. Odd. The dim thought rolled like a small wave in the back of his mind, subsided, and rolled again. Alice was getting old and was showing it. Now and then she forgot to do things. It didn't matter much, for she'd go on and do the next thing. It wasn't any more important than a skipped heartbeat, and there were lots of those. He guessed he was getting old too, but differently; he had all of his powers, only they were harder to call up, and it didn't make any difference if he didn't call them up, knowing they were there all right. Alice's powers seemed to vanish altogether every now and then, particularly lately, and at times there was a funny chill that beat outwards from her. It puzzled him a little, but not very much, the habit of their companionship being as old as it was. There was that strange cackle she had given when she had signed the deed with him that afternoon, and the unusual flourish of her pen at the end of her name.

An unusual day for them both, and important too, not because of anything that had been done, but because it had broken the routine and given him a chance to show that his powers were still unimpaired and that he could make decisions and act as well as he ever could. And none of it mattered, except for the inheritance taxes, which they had explained to him would be saved. He could see that in a flash and wanted them to see that he could see it. His nephew's wife hadn't needed to point it out to him so often.

"Not that you won't live for years and years," she had said, laughing briskly, "but – well, the time will come, you know, and after all we're younger and we're your only relatives too."

Yes, it was good business, he had said, raising his hand slowly and pulling at his ear; nothing else would be changed at all. He trusted her, even though she did look like a horse and had an annoying habit of parting her lips and then extending them stiffly, as if she were about to whinny. She and his nephew had moved in with them five years ago at least, he guessed it was, and had done nicely for them; good thing, help being so hard to find, and his nephew was a sober fellow

— a little pale, perhaps, and not much of a shakes at business, but he knew how to sit in a chair and not say much. Aletha, his wife, did what talking was needed, and it was usually to tell somebody to do something. A solid woman, if a little sharp. She helped Alice take care of her money too; the little they had was hers and it needed some watching. Perhaps Alice needed a little watching as well. When she had come home the other day saying with a shrill laugh that she had just bought a new fur coat and a second hand car, when she knew they didn't have the money in the bank and hadn't had a car for twenty years, Aletha had taken the affair in hand and straightened it out promptly and no more nonsense. Alice had sat by the fire and looked at a point just above it, as she was doing now, and hadn't seemed to remember when he spoke to her about it.

Well, there it was in black and white, and the inheritance taxes would be saved. The rest didn't matter. Henry and Aletha had made a great show of signing the contract to take care of him and Alice for the rest of their lives, but they had been doing it for five years and in the nature of things he and Alice had to have help. It went without saying. And the deed had been signed with great good humor; Alice first, since the house stood in her name, and she had grasped the pen like a dagger and pointed it at Aletha, and then laughed. She had always had a playful streak in her. They had all laughed, and he had stepped up and signed his name quickly, so the shake in his hand wouldn't show. Dear me, what difference did a few papers make to the house? It was his home, had been for as long as it had been built, and he'd always been able to pay the taxes.

He stirred in his chair. The fire was a dull red smudge in the ashes. He hoisted himself to his feet and took Alice by the hand. It seemed to take a while to rouse her, and when she got up her eyes were leaden and her teeth ground together with a little clicking noise. She followed him silently to bed and lay down quietly, making no sign as she usually did when he brushed his lips against her forehead. He sighed and stretched himself slowly between the sheets, letting out a little gasp when his head reached the pillow and his muscles relaxed. His arms and legs felt as fragile as if they were pinned to him, and his heart seemed to sit like a small shaking engine on his chest. The thin blanket of sleep settled tentatively about him.

He awoke suddenly, with the feeling that a sentinel had bent over and whispered to him sharply. A full moon was flooding the room, so like the silver mist at the edges of his field of vision that for a moment he could not separate them. There was something amiss in the familiar room. The silver light had gathered into a column beside his bed, and he shook his head to get it straight. As he did, his heart smote him like a hammer and he put out a trembling hand to light the bedlamp. He fumbled with it in his fright, but the white column beside him did not move. Then the yellow light burst from the lamp and he saw Alice standing in her nightgown, her eyes fixed dully on a point just above his head, and a knife upraised in one hand.

He stumbled somehow out of bed, his arm shaking while he reached for the knife. She was a tiny thing, hardly bigger than a candle, and her frail fingers yielded so easily that he took the knife from her without difficulty.

"Alice!" he exclaimed, his voice cracked and trembling. "What are you doing?"

She did not move her eyes from where they had been when he first saw her, and her shrunken lips were thin and blue.

"I thought you wanted to kill me," she said tonelessly.

He stared at her, his old eyes blinking while he tried to take it in. He was about to expostulate but closed his mouth again; probably a bad dream, but he didn't know, it was pretty queer. He murmured something that he couldn't catch himself, and led her back to her bed. She sank at once into a waxlike immobility and he sat down beside her, afraid to go to bed again and wondering what to do. After a while she opened her eyes and began to babble – snatches of things from their early life and even from before their marriage, and nonsense, and dirty things that hurt him, looking down at her sagging, distorted face. When the sun rose he was still huddled in his chair by her bed, trying to cope with the idea that after more than sixty years together his Alice had become insane.

When he thought it was decently late enough, he went to call Aletha and told her the story. She strode into the room, her hair in curl papers and her lips straight out.

"Well!" she said, snapping them together and pushing the air out from between them in a sharp blast. "Well, I never!"

Henry followed in a moment, tying himself up in his bathrobe. His hair was pushed together, by being slept on, from the sides of his head into a scalplock in the middle. They were a forlorn crew, but Aletha took command promptly.

"Well!" she said again, giving Henry a significant look. "Get dressed, both of you. We must take action."

She took action at breakfast, and it was definite. She fixed Professor Alberson with a determined eye.

"This is a little more than we bargained for," she announced. "Isn't it, Henry?"

Henry agreed that it was, his eyes on his plate.

"We shall have her put in a Home at once," she went on, raising her hand to prevent the objection in the old man's open mouth. "Oh yes, we will. You may risk your life if you wish, but we must consider ourselves as well. After our years of drudgery here, we have our rights. I will arrange everything." She dropped her voice to admit a tone of professional softness to enter it. "I have it all arranged in my mind. We will clear out the books in one of those rooms on the third floor and you can live there very comfortably. Or of course you may take her elsewhere if you wish; only I think my way is best." She smiled glitteringly and concluded with the air of patting down a grave: "We have the deed now, you know."

She had arisen before Professor Alberson could get it all clear in his head, and put on her hat and coat. She stood for a moment to thrust her hands into her gloves, the fingers wriggling like serpents under the pliant leather. He raised his head to speak to her but she had gone, followed precipitately by Henry. He groped his way upstairs, needing Alice in whatever condition she was; speech had become unnecessary between them for so long that her presence was enough. He couldn't see what Aletha was getting at. She was upset, of course; absurd, what she had said about clearing out that room on the third floor. Goodness me, his bedroom and his library – they couldn't be touched, naturally. He'd heard that people who went queer in the head sometimes had guardians appointed to look after their affairs; that's what Aletha was talking about, it would come out all right.

A few days later he was served with a notice to appear at the courthouse and give whatever testimony he might have in the matter of Alice Alberson, an alleged weak-minded person.

Aletha had gone to the first lawyer she could find, a bright young man so eager to do his work well that he made the mistake of letting Aletha's enthusiasm become his own and doing precisely what she wanted done. To his credit it might be said that Aletha did not tell him about the deed, perhaps because she didn't want to or because she thought she shouldn't, and to young Mr. Trask the case looked like a routine affair of having a guardian appointed. It did not occur to Aletha that if she petitioned the Court to have Alice declared mentally incompetent so soon after the execution of the deed, her position with respect to the property might be jeopardized.

During the interval before the hearing Professor Alberson had come to the painful conclusion that all was not well, but he could not see more than one step ahead and he had the confidence of the very old that everything would right itself in time. He decided to go to the hearing and enter his objection; that would do the trick with the least trouble and a minimum of hard feelings. He'd just put his foot down. He was Alice's husband, and he needed no lawyer to tell him how to settle a simple matter like that.

The hearing, however, was a failure. The two doctors who

had examined Alice a day or two before testified laconically that her case was one of senile dementia and that the prognosis was hopeless. Aletha knew exactly how much property Alice had and was able to provide details of her peculiar conduct over the past few months. Professor Alberson, a hand cupped behind his ear and peering up at the bench, had taken heart at first. A sign there told him that it was occupied by Judge Parkinson, and he was an old fellow, nearly as old as himself, he'd say. They'd understand one another; and when Mr. Trask said that he had finished, and paused, Professor Alberson got up and raised his hand. The judge, pen poised above his docket, said gruffly that he didn't care to be interrupted; but when the Professor insisted that he was the lady's husband, the judge sat back with a snort of impatience and told him to say what he had to say and get it over with quickly.

The professor took the stand and said that he entered an objection, and leaned back.

Parkinson fixed him with an irascible eye.

"Well, what of it?" he demanded.

"Your Honor," Professor Alberson began, a little confused, "we have lived together for over sixty years and she's very small and frail. I can take care of her, in our own home."

Mr. Trask, a little smile on his face, undertook to cross-examine. The knife, the fur coat, the second hand car, and a few other incidents were readily admitted. So was Professor Alberson's age. Mr. Trask drew down the corners of his mouth and nodded to the bench. Parkinson then began a long harangue about protecting the aged from themselves and about senile old men who ought to have guardians of their own. He got quite red and angry over it, and at the end he committed Alice to the County Home and at Mr. Trask's suggestion appointed Aletha as guardian of her property, with bond.[1]

"There," he stated, "now you know what's good for you. Adjourn Court."

But Professor Alberson had an attack of rage on his own account and turned to the bench, his stick raised menacingly.

"I'll not stand for this!" he shouted.

"Oh no?" said Parkinson. "What do you think you'll do about it?"

The two angry old men stood glaring at each other until Parkinson, saying something about the dignity of his Court and wasting his time, turned on his heel and disappeared.

"You'll see!" Professor Alberson shouted at his retreating back. He stamped out of court trembling with fury and fully aroused at last. They'd not take Alice, they'd not. He knew a lawyer too; and by good luck he found him in his office.

The lawyer was older than young Mr. Trask, and he inquired into the affairs of Aletha and Henry. When he had heard the story of the deed and the contract he leaned back and rested his tired eyes on Professor Alberson's face with a flicker of affectionate amusement.

"Now why on earth," he asked, "did you go off to that hearing all by yourself and object to it?"

Professor Alberson peered at him anxiously.

"But, but — " he began, spreading his wrinkled hands.

---

1 Guardians must put up a bond — cash, unencumbered real estate, or the obligation of an approved bonding company — to prevent their running off with the assets of their ward and to ensure their preservation. Trust companies, when they act as guardians, may sign their own bonds, on the theory that they are solvent, conservative, and likely to remain in one place.

"Yes, I know," his friend went on, "you don't have to tell me. Only it makes our work harder. Now you've got to go back into court as fast as I can get you there and swear that she was incompetent. Fortunately you admitted the facts under cross-examination today. You sit there; I'm going to dictate a bill in equity to have the deed set aside because of mental incapacity and undue influence, with an injunction on affidavits [1] to stop their taking your wife to the Home. After that we'll have to persuade Parkinson to vacate that part of his decree." He stopped and shook his head sadly. "That will be the hardest part of our job. Now sit there quietly and don't disturb me."

When the papers were completed he grabbed his hat and disappeared. Half an hour later he returned.

"Everything's all right," he said, putting his hand on Professor Alberson's thin shoulder and squeezing it gently. "Judge Ulen has signed the injunction, but it's on affidavits only and there has to be a hearing within four days. I'll see him again to fix the time definitely and I'll let you know. Come along now. I'm going home with you," he concluded grimly, "and see that a copy of this gets served properly on Aletha and Henry."

---

[1] An injunction is an order, signed by a judge, telling someone to stop doing something, or else. It is granted, of course, after full hearing. But there are cases in which the damage would be done if time for hearing were taken: a person might be wrongfully evicted from his home and find himself on the street if he could not do something very quickly. In such case he files a bill in equity and attaches a required number of affidavits to the effect that the facts are true and the danger imminent. If the judge decides that the bill shows a case on its face he signs the injunction, but it is good only for a few days and a hearing must be held within that time. Such an injunction preserves the status quo when it would be outrageous to disturb it.

They went to the street and got a cab. Professor Alberson was very tired and he had no more appetite for judges. He asked a few questions about Ulen, which the lawyer answered briefly. "No, he's not old," he added, and heard his friend sigh. "Maybe that will be an advantage." But Professor Alberson didn't know; he thought that he ought to be able to rely on old men.

When they reached home, Aletha and Henry had almost finished clearing out the room on the third floor. Their lips tightened when they saw the injunction but they said nothing. The lawyer looked at them reflectively.

"Your contract to take care of the Professor and his wife," he observed, "is still good. He will notify me at once if you fail to do so, and I'll have the law on you further. It's to your interest to behave, at least until this thing is ironed out. When it is, I have ideas of my own about how they will be looked after, right here and without your further interference."

When the lawyer had left, Professor Alberson climbed slowly to his room and lay down on his bed. Alice was still in hers, and the house reached out for him as if nothing had happened. It might still come out all right, only he was not sure any longer, but wary, and it hurt him; he seemed to be digging up the old years and distressing them. It all depended on that young judge now; how could he know the sweetness and temper of those old years and what they had built up between him and Alice? How could anyone else know that? Not that it had ever mattered before, but it mattered now, and his security had suddenly flown from his hands into those of an unknown young man who had the power to let Alice be taken from him. A young man, barely half his age; it was in his hands now. He hoped it would be all for the best.

The thin blanket of sleep did not drift down upon him until nearly dawn.

It didn't take Ulen long to read the papers. The bill stated in effect that Alberson and his wife owned a house and had deeded it to the Porters in return for personal services. Ulen frowned. They should have filed a more specific bill; personal services might mean anything. Deed – undue influence – fraud – wife mentally incompetent. Prayer [2] to restrain further conveyance and to compel reconveyance. He flipped back the pages; oh yes, the house had been in her name. Prayer to restrain the respondents from removing the wife to the County Home, despite Judge Parkinson's decree. Gosh, that was difficult. He tossed the bill across his desk and took up the testimony. Routine, all of this, he said to himself. Hm. The old lady was eighty-two, but she had a little money. Two doctors had testified and so had one of the respondents: delusions, senile dementia, something about a knife – usual stuff. Judge Parkinson had found her incompetent and ordered her committed to the County Home.

He felt a vague irritation, having covertly to review Parkinson's work. It was a burden all of the other judges had to share discreetly now and then. Parkinson didn't care, really; he needed the salary and held on to his position by making

[2] A remnant, I believe, of the practise of addressing one's complaint direct to the king and asking him for relief. The litigant who files a bill in equity asks the Court to do certain things for him; these requests are called prayers.

loud noises, but he didn't care, and his law clerk wrote all of his opinions. Ulen decided that he had better not talk to him until after the hearing. It was an emergency and fraud was alleged – excuse enough for acting first and explaining later. But old – what was his name? – Alberson, how did he expect to get away with objecting before Parkinson and now coming in to upset everything by relying on the very mental incompetence that he had objected to Parkinson's finding? Oh hell, he was tired; he couldn't tell until he heard it.

He skidded the testimony over the desk towards the other papers and leaned back in his chair. His eyes closed and he could feel the minutes slipping away like sand down the sides of a pile. Lord, he had trouble enough getting at a case in court; these papers were dull and meant little. Time enough tomorrow. He let them fade from his mind and lay slack, thinking about old men. Generally they were abrupt, when their attention was captured, and capturing it was not an easy thing to do. They seemed to creep along under a heavy coverlet of time and only now and then find a hole to pop their head out of suddenly and make reply before sinking again. Emerging that way often irritated them, and one wondered what their life had been, to make the present moment so unpalatable. He guessed he had Parkinson too much on his mind; all old men weren't like that. Parkinson hadn't grown up and still wanted to be a boy; finding that he was too stiff to be one made him angry, and he put all of the strength he had left into his voice.

Michael hadn't been like that. Ulen rolled his head against the cushioned back of his chair and felt better at the thought of Michael. He hadn't been nearly as old as Parkinson when he died and he hadn't really aged at all; he had simply whitened slowly into death, and there had seemed to be no difference in him when they found him in the morning, except that he was lifeless.

That was the way Michael had hoped it would be, although he never said so, knowing that he would be the first one of the household to go. For their sakes he had tried to reduce his death to the status of a short fact and he had done it by seeking to arrest within himself the sense of personal attachment to life. Changelessly meeting change without surprise, he had managed to give them the feeling that his death would be only another change and not a finality, and he succeeded because he had made of his life the career of an idea. He had been more silent than usual during the evening when he knew, as the chronically ill do, that his time had come. His attention came and went, despite him; that meant that time was clotting. He rubbed his hands together gently, to center himself for a moment. Possibly he could sleep before the center broke. He would like that, not having the full arc interrupted, even at the end. He looked about him wearily, and a smile rose but did not reach the surface of his face. He knew that they would let him do it in his own way, but he thought that the concession of a word was necessary; best not to surprise people who were still surprisable, despite what he had obliquely tried to teach them.

"I think it is time for me to die," he said, getting up slowly, and made his way upstairs.

"Michael!" Mrs. Ulen said in a low voice. She sat back and watched him. She couldn't know but she couldn't let him go alone. Half way up the stairs he turned slightly and let the smile come to the surface. She smiled back, her eyes full on him.

In his room he sat down heavily on his bed and looked for a moment at his long, white hands, thinking. Then he lay down, fully clothed, and turned off the light. The tiny drumbeat within him was low and unsteady, and there was a feeling of the center moving outwards. With a flicker of amusement he reached up and closed his eyelids with his fingers, then crossed his hands against his chest. The center was rushing from him, and sleep came quickly, like a shadow.

Ulen took a long breath and stirred in his chair. Oh man, he said to himself; he had heard his wife speak to Michael that evening and had raised his eyes at the tone in her voice. But she hadn't got up and he had gone on reading. He'd missed quite a great moment, he thought, but she hadn't, and he was glad of that. He opened his eyes and they fell on the papers that he had tossed across his desk. He leaned forward to put them in order. He was glad he had a case for tomorrow. He was going to bring Julia to town, for she liked coming to court for a very little while and making faces at him, knowing that he couldn't return them. They were tentative faces; they grew slowly and suddenly disappeared when they threatened to get out of hand and become noticeable. He chuckled, and good humor sent up little ripples from the deep pit of his fatigue.

He scratched his head. Guessed he'd go over to the museum for half an hour and look at the geology exhibit. It soothed him with its comfortable long waves of time. He remembered getting a notice about some new material they had on the Archaean Period. It was so fabulously long ago and covered such an incalculable period of time that it would crush smooth the gravelled lumps of hours that had made his day. Yes, he'd do that. He got to his feet, stretching his shoulders, put on his hat and coat, and went out.

XII

Julia

THE NEWS of Ulen's accident, boiled down to a precise point of fact, came to this:

". . . Judge Ulen and his daughter, aged four, were struck from behind by a drunken driver who swerved his car onto the sidewalk where they were walking and crushed them against the building. The judge had just bent over to pick up a doll the child had dropped when they were struck. The little girl was killed instantly, and it is believed that Ulen was seriously injured, for he was unconscious when picked up by passers-by. On the way to the hospital he roused for a moment and was heard to murmur something about the weather clearing. . . ."

◇◇◇◇◇◇◇◇◇◇◇◇◇

Ulen alighted from the train and turned to guide Julia down the steps. The small hand buried in his felt like a firm ripe peach.

Once a month, as a reward for good behavior, she was permitted to go to town with her father and turn his office upside down for approximately an hour before Mrs. Ulen, subdued from marketing, arrived to take her to dancing class.

He looked down, checking rubbers, a mitten hanging by a string from each sleeve, the visible bright heads of buttons, a morose and battered doll. All present. The trip had not been without incident. Julia had staged a small but powerful rebellion when she discovered that he had a ticket of his own and she had none. It wasn't fair, she managed to observe from under an avalanche of sobs. He hadn't looked at it just that way before, and the effort to explain it adequately had left him a little breathless.

"Well, Mrs. 'Opkins," he remarked, gathering himself, "now that you have me in town, what are you going to do with me?"

The child turned up a delighted face. New adventure was wonderful and a bit alarming, and the offer to direct so large and formidable a creature as a father called for a quick look of trust that he didn't really mean it. One was very little and the city muttered ominously. Adventure by ritual, however, was a wave-beat on the shore of Heaven, but with the world so alive and fresh the quick look had to be included just in case. Ulen read it and smiled reassuringly.

"Come along," he said. "Today I have to be in court, and as a special treat you may go with me. Miss Dingle will come too, and you must stay with her and be quiet and do just what she says."

Julia's eyes grew big.

"Will you put on your bathrobe?" she asked.

"That," Ulen responded severely, "is not a bathrobe. It is a judicial robe, and you must get up when I come in."

Julia trudged.

"All the way up?" she inquired after a moment. "Wouldn't a little bounce do, like you when Mummy comes in the room?"

"Feet," said Ulen, somewhat stiffly. "Both feet, no thumb in the mouth, and no bounce."

"Well," Julia replied, "all right. I'll make faces at you until Mummy comes and gets me."

"I won't have much time to look at you," he remarked. "You won't mind, will you? Be nice to Miss Dingle; and Mummy will come soon."

"I like Miss Dingle," Julia said. "Once she had a piece of candy." Her curls jiggled while she weighed the chances and stole an appraising glance upward. "She gave it to me. She said she might do it again. Isn't that silly?" The rear-guard action continued without interruption. "I thaid silly right."

Ulen saw no reason not to fall for it.

"You said thaid," he observed.

"I didn't. I said thilly and didn't stick my tongue out."

"Hold it up so just the end can wiggle, only don't wiggle it, and almost close your teeth."

Julia looked up accusingly. "You said teeth."

"Oh damn," said Ulen, "that's what they are. Tease is when you step on the cat."

They walked on in silence for a minute.

"Of course girls of four don't step on cats," he added.

"But I am a little bit five," Julia argued, nodding her head in great arcs. She laboriously shifted her grip on the doll and grew thoughtful. "Daddy," she said, sighing with the effort of forcing an idea in flight through the small hole of her vocabulary, "when I grow up will I slow down or get quicker?"

"You'll do both," he answered. "You'll be like the engine that tried to go over the mountain: the upper it went the downer it slowed. But you'll see more because you're up higher. You can go quicker when you can see more." He felt that he was getting mixed up and changed the subject. "Here is our fat friend with the newspapers. I want to buy one."

The newsboy engaged Ulen in conversation. He was a voluble young man of Polish ancestry, and the heavy sibilant accent poured over them in a flood. When he turned to take care of another customer Julia giggled. The long lip forced up her nose as if she were pointing with it. "He talks the same words we do but not the same tune," she said in a stage whisper, squinting at the newsboy. "Tell me the story of him again."

"In a moment," Ulen promised. He completed the transaction and they escaped through a sudden crowd of purchasers. He took a deep breath, for he didn't like repeating stories and Julia liked nothing better. He gazed thoughtfully into the distance. The span of attention was short and he wouldn't have to go far. Julia was gazing at him expectantly.

"Once upon a time," he declaimed, "there was a very fat boy who looked as if his clothes had been put on with a shovel."

"Why?" Julia interrupted.

"Because he was very poor," Ulen continued, unruffled, "and that is all he had to put his clothes on with. Well, one day — " He became aware of pressure from the small hand holding his. He looked down and saw Julia come to a halt like the sudden dropping of a breeze, her whole vitality centered for a moment in her eyes. He looked ahead. They were in the middle of a block and the traffic light at the corner had turned red.

"Red means stop," Julia said firmly.

"Come along," he urged. "That's only when we're at corners. Wait a minute. You dropped your doll. I'll get it."

As he stooped to rescue it there was a slight click in his ears. His fingers were closing on the doll, but it seemed to jump ahead a little, and there was a tiny whirlwind of dust where it had lain. He reached for it and picked it up, telling himself crossly that he was getting old. He dusted the toy with his sleeve and handed it back to Julia.

"There you are, Mrs. 'Opkins," he said. "Hold her tight so she won't turn into a pig and run off when you drop her again."

"When I was very young," Julia said seriously, "I did turn into a pig once, but then I woke up. It was dark and you and Mummy came in. I couldn't find a good dream. Why did you and Mummy come in?"

"To turn you into a little girl again," Ulen replied. "We like you better without the grunt."

"Would I still be a pig if you hadn't come in?" Julia asked, a little anxiously.

"You might, but I think you could have managed it by yourself. Sometimes at the table I wonder if there wasn't just a little bit we missed."

She skipped ahead of him on the pavement, jerking her arms stiffly out from her body, then paused and turned thoughtfully to wait for him. "Will Mummy come for me to-day, soon?"

"Oh, Mummy won't come for a long time," he replied. "But we can ask Uncle Michael about it. Here he is."

Michael was approaching and came to a stop before them. He looked taller and straighter than usual, and his light suit shone in the sunshine. Julia ran to him and buried her face against his knees, then lifted her head without moving her body and slowly said: "Hello."

Michael put his fingers under her chin and looked down at her. His face was dark but he held her gaze for a moment intently. Then he lifted his eyes to Ulen and gently disengaged himself.

"She will be in good hands," he said and passed on.

Julia looked after him before recapturing her father's hand, and they walked down the long street past the policeman at the corner. The houses thinned at last and they saw the pavement end in the bronze autumn undergrowth of the field beyond.

"Let's explore," said Julia.

Ulen paused at the edge of the field and let his eyes range about in it. It stretched broadly before them until it rose into a hill with a crown of tall trees on top. A low cloud had caught in them and was held there. Julia reached impatiently for her father and drew him after her. They scuffed their feet in the brittle fallen leaves and stopped to watch the smoke rising blue and fat from burning piles. At first they spoke little, for there was much to see in the busy vacancy of the country, and instinctively they turned towards the hill, as if the attention of the earth had gathered in it and there were no other place a man and a little girl would go. Julia romped about, peering into holes, and froze into a solid look when an animal broke cover near them and bounded for a thicket. The look arced up to her father.

"Rabbit," said Julia.

Ulen followed the retreating animal with his eyes. "I'm afraid I disturbed him," he said, "but he isn't really frightened; his ears are still up."

She scampered off and Ulen could see her small stern while she poked about in a bush or bent double over a patch of high seed-grass. He sauntered up the hill, sobered momentarily by the rabbit's sudden motion, and let his thoughts wander. A slight chill stole down the slope when he neared the trees, and the sun dimmed behind the cloud. He turned back to wait for Julia, who raised herself at length and looked about her until she caught sight of him. Then she started towards him, arms hanging loose and knees pushing forward wearily. When she reached him she heaved a large sigh and wagged her head widely.

"No rabbits," she announced.

"Maybe we'll find some in the woods," Ulen said, nodding towards them.

Julia looked up at him.

"You carry me," she said, holding out her arms, "I'm tired."

He laughed and stooped down.

"Right, Mrs. 'Opkins," he agreed. "Up you come."

He put one arm around her back and the other under her legs, nestling her head into the crook of his elbow. He stood there for a moment, smiling down at her. She looked back soberly until her gaze drifted off to the clouds above them.

Then her eyes closed and her breathing deepened. He bent his head and rubbed her forehead gently with his chin.

"Whiskers," Julia murmured sleepily. She grew limp in his arms and gave off the fleeting mealy smell of a sleeping child. One fat hand pressed softly against his coat. He held her to him and walked up the hill, looking about him contentedly. He made out a slight path that he could follow and when he entered the woods the fog swirled about him, shrouding the tree trunks and dampening his face.

Julia stirred closer to him. She was an easy burden and he felt strong and light. The trees lifted vague arms high above them and the fog closed in, bellying towards him in thick gusts, which now and then hid even Julia from him. He tightened his hold on her a little and walked forwards steadily, watching the white mist flow about him until he could no longer see the path and had to raise his eyes for direction to the dim aisle of trees. The melting air thickened. It's only a cloud, he said to himself, and lifted his eyebrows while the thought drifted through his mind.

"It will clear soon," he said aloud. "You watch."

THE BOOK:

I Too, Nicodemus

I

I Too, Nicodemus

THE LAW SUFFERS from being thought of as an intellectual profession.

It is intellectual, of course. The mind's bite when it seeks the length and limits of a rule is exhilarating, particularly when something depends upon it. At times the result is tangible and at others it is as intangible as the effects of education. But it is not scientific in the sense of a science whose rules are impersonal and beyond the reach of human emotion or behavior. Emotion and behavior are the raw material from which the law is distilled in one way or another, and he gets to be known as a scientific lawyer who forgets that the raw material and the law are of the same substance.

There are signs that familiar ideas of the law are changing. It is elementary in legal philosophy that customs are more faithfully observed than laws, and it seems to be true that a country with many customs has relatively few laws. Modern civilization and war tend to destroy customs, and where the steadying force of custom disappears laws increase apace.

They also increase in a country where particular accent is placed upon the rights and development of individual people, for average behavior tends to break up into original behavior and laws are needed to control the new lines of activity for the sake of the general welfare. Particularly when the general welfare includes the notion that extreme economic positions should be avoided.

The increased volume of laws means less legal certainty. The Constitution is the framework of a picture that is constantly being painted, and it is the courts that finally say what the law is. Every time a court case is decided the Constitution is amended just a little: the only difference between court decisions and constitutional amendments as such is the size of the question involved. As personal originality advances, average conduct blurs, and so does the law. It becomes no longer so easy to predict what courts will do, since they are psychologically equipped to declare and enforce average behavior.

The only healthy development of this process seems to be that people should manage to make themselves better understood. Since life has a strange way of providing compensations, even this is being arranged – for individuals if not for groups. The doctors' increasingly personal treatment of people has its analogy in the law. The effect of this pressure can be seen most easily in the lowest legal cells, the police and magistrates'[1] courts, where there is a refreshing simplicity of

[1] Also called squires and justices of the peace. After the arresting officer, they are your first contact with the law. They hold you for Court if there appears to be a case against you, but they do not usually hear your side. They can send people to jail in minor offenses for short periods and can decide small business cases involving a limited amount of money. Usually they are

procedure and freedom from rules. If the truth were known, the law of the books is being bent every day in these lowest tribunals, in order to fit it to the needs of the community: It was Nathan that once shouted provocatively at Ulen that all judges were in the wrong places. The best legal brains should be magistrates, he asserted vigorously, since they are closest to people's problems and have to deal with them raw; the next best should be in the trial courts; and any young essay writers just out of law school would do as appellate judges, since it requires only technicians to provide a system of *stare decisis* [2] and the street would ultimately adapt the law to itself anyway.

Be this as it may, there can be no sensitive judge who does not feel that the growing will and power of the individual citizen to assert himself is pushing the old rules of procedure and evidence to the wall. The better informed people become, the less patient they are of restrictions whose reason is

---

not required to be lawyers and therefore their decisions can have an air of oddity about them, but they have great power over the daily lives and affairs of ordinary people, for they can cause an unholy amount of inconvenience. They like being called "Judge."

[2] To stand by the decisions. Appellate judges get frightfully worked up about this, since it involves the main reason for their existence. The English Common Law grew by the creeping analogy of case to case, and after the same rule had been applied to a number of similar situations, people came to act in reliance on it, particularly in connection with property. In those days there were few statutes. Now there are a great many, and the same process of creeping analogy is applied to their interpretation, especially when they are written, as the Constitution is, in general language. It is regarded as unfair and unwise to alter these decisional rules and interpretations arbitrarily or abruptly, although chipping bits from them is permissible, and because life is apt to treat them much more rudely, it is necessary to do so in order to bring the law reasonably abreast of the times. And sometimes the chips grow into new rules which supersede the old ones.

not readily apparent to them, and the wisdom of legal rules, gathered from the stretch of experience, is beginning to break against the single rock of the case at hand. The tendency is to decide each case by what is fair and to hold the law in reserve, where it can be resorted to when experience clearly counts or where, as always, it is effective to resort to it. The two rules most directly concerned are the rule of relevance and the ban on hearsay [3] evidence.

Irrelevance can be highly enlightening. The witness who starts with what she had for breakfast and remembers it was Thursday because her husband's sister had come down with the measles when she shouldn't have if she had only gone to the other doctor, the one with glasses – should be a delight to the judge's heart and make the jury feel at home. Behind this leisurely sweep of incident they can follow her as they please, and it will give them at least her barometric pressure at the time when she signed the note at the bank without reading it. After listening to enough of it, any idiot would know that she was an accommodation endorser [4] who had done it to help her husband and had got nothing out of it for herself, but if the judge and jury are presented with a dry handful of disconnected facts they can't be so sure. Facts alone are a

[3] The witness who tries to tell the jury what Mrs. Jones said will be told sternly that he mustn't, unless the fact of her speaking is the point at issue, apart from the truth of what she said. The law thinks it isn't fair, because Mrs. Jones isn't present to be observed and cross-examined. But most likely the fact of her not being called to speak for herself would be as devastating as any supposed advantage accruing from reporting her *in absentia.* Oddly enough, juries do have intelligence.

[4] One who endorses another person's note in order to help him get credit, but gets no advantage out of it himself. He may get a good deal of disadvantage, as he will be liable if the principal doesn't pay. Sometimes a married woman can sign to help her husband and escape liability if he doesn't pay.

skeleton, and when a judge reads over a record with only facts in it, it sits like a skeleton in his lap and grins at him horridly. Ulen mistrusted very thin men and very thin records.

As for hearsay, it is of the very flavor of the ordinary citizen's life, and the ordinary citizen sits in the jury box. If things are kept from him he supplies decisive theories of his own, for after all he is there to solve cases and is conscientiously determined to do so as well as he can. And he seems to know that no one can ask him how he does it. Floods of harmless hearsay are allowed to pass every day, with the result that when an objection is made the jury are all ears and their imaginations set to work. Subject to judicial discretion and to proper comment by judge and counsel, juries could evaluate hearsay evidence better than they are given credit for. Particularly if a wider cross-section of the community were compelled to serve. It was Ulen's experience that the more juries heard of the full story, the more accurate their verdicts were apt to be. Accurate according to his own view, of course, but they also rested well with the courtroom audience.

The law has been able to manage average behavior quite well, but if it is to manage unique behavior it must leave more room. When it does, greater freedom will be allowed an increasingly educated public to evolve its law from the bottom. It is from what happens in the magistrates' courts and trial courts that appellate and legislative law is moulded in the long run. To keep this process fluid and accurate requires as simple a court procedure as possible and the elimination of the rules of evidence beyond what is inherently fair and generally germane. Trial judges must admit that this is what happens in half of their run of the mine cases every day, while the great legal rules slumber, waiting for the *cause célèbre* to invoke them on behalf of somebody's special or intense interest and threaten to turn the trial into an ordeal by counsel [5] or a bear-trap for the unwary.

Ulen had come to adopt a motto when he was in court: "Use as little law as possible." There is more in people's minds, when they go to law, than the hope that a set of rules will produce the result they desire. If that were true, it would be possible to write a code capable of providing for every contingency. Beyond the hope of winning the case there is the faint magic of the theater, and a little of the church too, and a good deal of school to be suffered on the way. People do not go to law primarily to feel these satisfactions, but without always knowing it they look for them in the courtroom, and he is a wise judge who provides them if he can. The setting is there: God is invoked in the oath, and over the months there is no other place where His name is mentioned so often, even in Church; the witness stand is a stage, and many an actor gives a superlative performance there, straight out of life; and from the Bench comes teaching in the things that hold

[5] A feeble attempt at humor by me. Many centuries ago, really many, before there was a jury system, law suits were settled by ordeal. There was the ordeal by battle, when the parties fought each other, personally or by champion. There was the ordeal by fire, held in Church with full service: the accused had to carry red hot metal nine paces down the aisle, and the rate at which his burns healed determined his guilt or innocence. And there was the ordeal by water. The accused was bound and thrown in the lake: if he was pure, Sister Water received him unto herself and he was declared innocent, although he incidentally drowned during the process. If he was impure and Sister Water rejected him so that he floated, he was declared guilty and put to death without further ado. The modern combat between skilled lawyers, often at the expense of justice, might be called ordeal by counsel.

society together, and these things should be the law at its best. Once Court opens, the shadow of illusion descends upon it, as it does upon any scene of reconstruction, and the inquiry is not only whether things were done, but why. No one can answer that stubborn question with facts or arguments, but with his spirit only. And those with enough experience in court know that in every case the question does get answered, well or badly. It is not enough to send men and women away from court with a decision; there must also be a sense that there is wisdom in it, and a blessing upon it, and a touch of kindly magic to go with it.

Hence Ulen's preoccupation with things not to be found in law books – the Bay, and silence, and religion, and people, and what went on inside of little Julia. Hence too the evolution of his motto, which he believed would allow people to be more fully trusted in court – trusted to lie and cheat and be truthful and honorable in very much the same way as they acted at home, and to be judged accordingly. He thought that his legal judgments should not be dooms, and that the Irish, who invented that word for them, must have done so more in anguish than in satisfaction, they knowing more than most of us do about the vagaries of the Little People in our lives.

The law must retain its character as a wistful promise if it is not to become a bludgeon altogether. At its best it offers a collective promise, and in sorrow it allows for private promises too, for no man exacts a promise from another unless he mistrusts him, or gives one unless he mistrusts himself. And because a man will break his promise with colder deliberation than he will kill or rob, the law of contract is essentially penal, and the law of crime is essentially contractual. We live every moment of our lives under the promises of our representatives that we will do no harm, but it is only now and then that we commit a contract, and we sign our names to its specific sanctions. So greatly do we trust or want to trust our fellows that no man makes a promise not to assault his neighbor, but he is willing to live under such a promise and consent to it as law. The real mistrust in people for each other appears in their contracts and in the economic penalties that have been specially constructed for their enforcement. To use as little law as possible is to take a long step towards giving people back their confidence in themselves and in each other, for most of them are decent enough to have an instinctive dislike of laws.

The law is indeed a kind of promise. Even the old talonic law, if it is read rightly, promised no more than an eye for an eye or one tooth for one tooth; it was an advance on the times. In ancient Locris a man who proposed a law in the popular assembly did so on a platform with a rope around his neck. If his law passed, they removed the rope: if it failed, they removed the platform. It was as if the people of ancient Locris did not want to promise too much. One can learn, even from the pagans. We seem no longer to care in that way. We are losing the sense of the value of a promise by making it easy to get around the ones we have, by bankruptcy and statutes of limitation and divorce. We are loosening a man's word by giving him mere liberty and there is something wrong with that. Liberalism is not looseness. It requires severe personal discipline and a view of tolerance that is like

Montaigne's – the effort to make decency prevail – rather than the view that anything goes.

There is no plea to be made except to keep the law personal. Those in its high places must be careful lest they forget people and remember only the machinery that governs them. Some do forget. There are some – and like as not they are known as liberals – to whom the law is a flashing plaything of the mind; but the point is not to change our systems but to use the ones we have as exquisitely as possible. Revolution is a protest against method, not against principle. To others the law is an engine driven by nothing but little gears, and to a great many it is simply an infuriating mass of negatives. Ulen tried to regard it as a necessary substitute for intuitive good living, to be used sparingly or withdrawn altogether whenever possible.

Many strange things have been made to grow up around the law by people who are obsessed by it. One of the most sonorous bits of nonsense is the aphorism that we live under a government of laws and not of men. It is hard to stay sober under this onslaught of sounding brass, but William Penn did, and he gave the answer to it. "Governments," he said, "like clocks, go from the motion men give them; and as governments are made and moved by men, so by them they are ruined too. Wherefore governments rather depend upon men than men upon governments. Let men be good and the government cannot be bad; if it be ill, they will cure it. But if men be bad, let the government be ever so good, they will endeavor to warp and spoil it to their turn."

Actually, we live under a government not so much of either

laws or men, but of ideas. That must be said, for we forget. Laws and inventions and public opinion are ideas, but once they are given separate names they take on separate connotations and significance, and we move away from the common base towards the shadows where things and names for things get mixed up. A judge must stay clear of that, or the first thing he knows his own ideas will come wriggling over the bench like the tentacles of an octopus and squeeze the breath out of everyone in court. Sometimes they should, and it takes an artist to know when, for it is usually better that the ideas of the parties should prevail so far as possible.

The law is more a point of view than a science, or even a system. Too much is usually claimed for it, even in the phrase Law and Order; as though given Law, Order will follow. It is rather the other way, that since people desire Order they have invented Law to help preserve it. This is a vital distinction, for the warlike history of the race does not allow us to take the desire for peace too much for granted. But the race has gone a respectable distance. A family needs no public law to keep the peace; its members can live in a pure state of anarchy, so far as law goes, and be at peace with one another. So can a very small community, but with larger growth comes the need for law, since many of the inhabitants are strangers to each other. Thus far we have been able to grow as large as nations and substitute law for force, and to agree that private warfare shall be settled in the arena of a court. But in the very large nations that idea blurs a little, and it is more precise to say that such communities are willing to trade a certain amount of violence for law; for there is crime and overreaching within the big groups, and these are forms of violence, and therefore the idea that law is preferable becomes a point of view. This is a considerable achievement.

Ulen's religious approach to peace was that men must be inwardly peaceful before they can become so outwardly, and his professional approach was that if private law were well enough administered, it would in time be adopted internationally as the best method of settling the causes of public warfare. This can happen only if people have confidence in the administration of their law, and since they have no idea that law is supernatural, the job rests squarely upon the spirit of those who do administer it. Each case a work of art, so far as possible, and not an act of grace or a scientific demonstration. That way lies aridity and madness; the effort to impose upon any large section of mankind a formula more definite than a point of view has driven men beyond their reason or has made brutes of them. And to impose judgment on a single man is to take away a little of the best of him.

Every trial represents a center of consent. Anyone that goes to court can see that the two or three aged bailiffs, who are there on the theory that they could put down riots, could not handle a determined effort to throw the courtroom into an uproar and upset the trial altogether. This happens very rarely; jail breaks and prison riots occur more frequently. It is not a full answer to say that the police could ultimately enforce the peace in court. Beyond this knowledge, people have accepted the idea that their disputes not only must be but are best resolved by law. It represents a real point of view about peace and war, and about order.

And about fresh beginnings too, which is only another name for rebirth. Most of us do not know what it is like to be on trial for our lives or liberty, or even for our veracity or reputation or segments of our bank account. There is no room in court for pride, and it is the pride in us that dislikes being judged, ever. Yet it is only when pride has been scraped away that fresh beginnings are possible, and those who work in court must remember if they can that every litigant leaves some of his spirit's skin outside and hence is the more sensitive to whatever is done to him. The opportunity of the judge to teach is great, and at times there comes an even greater one: to raise his hands and let them fall again, for the greatest judging lies in knowing when to say no word at all.

It is here, at the point of the greatest judging, that the law can cease to be a matter of rule and compensation and reach the realm of the intangibles: gentleness of heart, with clarity of mind and the quiet salt of faith. Not only judges, but lawyers too; and all men, in whatever it is they do. The command that they judge not, lest they be judged, is more than a special law of conduct. It is also a cry to the race not to compel judgment by one another. There is no sensitive judge who does not feel that all men, himself included, walk a little lower because of what the criminals whom he sentences have done. Their real crime is not to be found in the indictment, but it is implicit there: that they have made it necessary to judge them and so have tarnished those who do it. It is in such ways that we stain each other, and a man must run far to escape from judging somehow. Those who judge themselves, or can be helped to do so, lift the common burden by a little, and helping them requires some process of the spirit to re-imagine the ground they walk upon and to try to make them see it. Intuitive good living, that needs no judge beyond the circle of an inner light, is what Councill meant when he said that he believed in innocence but not in right and wrong, and that it is a matter of the distance one can see.

The law is not enough, nor can it be. It may even be too little for the best advance of the spirit, since it makes a business of judging, and a public one at that. The threat of spiritual sterility is great. The lofty, god-like judge who graciously unbends to the janitor, the judge who is so adept at misusing his time that he accuses everyone of wasting it, the bellowing and haranguing judge, the cynical and sneering judge who believes that he knows criminals because he has tried ten thousand of them, the hanging judge – these abominations of the Bench are simply sterile men, the more dangerous for their sterility because they are deceptively active and lively. For all their teeming incompetence, a grain of curiosity would go farther – some thirst for the innate authority in man, a sense that fresh beginning is possible, at all times, for all men, and in all conditions.

It must have been this kind of curiosity that accounts for the old and wealthy Nicodemus going by night to find out the authority of the young man from Galilee and perhaps to get a sign. That he could recognize neither the authority nor the sign when they were given is the central tragedy, and all of us are sons and daughters of Nicodemus.

The two men talked in hints and parables, as was Jesus' wont, and it is to the credit of the great Rabbi that he was intelligent enough to follow, up to a point, and humble enough to accept the method and the greatness of the younger man. One can see them sitting alone in the booth above Jesus' house, or it may have been, as one writer has it, in a cave on the top of the David Wall, the home of Hillel, the water-carrier. There must have been a fire, with shadows flowing and melting on their faces, and a long view over the Kidron Valley. It is certain that Jesus looked out at it and heard the wind afoot in it, for he spoke of the blowing air and likened man's spirit to it, telling his visitor not to marvel that he must be born again, since every man can be born of water and of the Spirit. Both together. And there, at the pivot of a living faith, Nicodemus faltered, as one must who stands too firmly on the law, and asked how such things could be. Jesus must have turned to him with a cry of anguish: "Are you a master in Israel and do not know these things?"

It adds to Jesus' stature as a teacher that he rose above his pain and went on to explain again; only the white fire was gone from him, and his eyes must have been on the embers before him when he chided Nicodemus for not coming to the light lest his deeds should be reproved, for the great Rabbi was at best a secret disciple. But it was as if Nicodemus were no longer there. There is no further word from him, which is a pity. But more than pity, for the world since has done little better than he; and possibly that adds to his stature too, so unexpected are the ways of compassion. I too, Nicodemus. It is our curiosity that may save us for further patient teaching.

Later, if we can believe the same writer, Nicodemus stood up for Jesus like a lion at the night trial in the Sanhedrin and demolished the prosecution's case as an expert lawyer would do. But all he had then was the law, and the law was not enough, even the moral law. It is a fragile thing in the hands of politicians. Nicodemus won every legal point but lost his case: Hanan, the High Priest, raised his finger and gave Jesus over to Rome, law or no law. Nicodemus' rebirth had failed, but Jesus' had begun. It has been so ever since, and with the ordinary children of men no rebirth is ever wholly clear and sure. A man's essential pattern does not change, and that is what makes his rebirths seem uncertain. But if he makes the best use of the present moment he will seem to be continually in birth, which is perhaps as near as he can approach a wholly fresh beginning. To sense this upward inner drift is the work of the great judge, and it is a work of art that forwards the progress of the race directly, since the world will always be a reflection of what men are within themselves.

To Ulen it was not a question of being good or seeing to it that others were. Goodness was not enough, as food without salt is not enough. Religious people always seemed to be hunting for something to torment themselves with or for a larger bosom to cast themselves upon and bleed, and the mystics were lost in a world of their own. A man's last loneliness is his own full integrity, if he knows what it is, and it is possible to have faith that it is good. Ulen thought of Perle and Joe living quietly and constructively in sin, and felt that the law was not yet wise enough to measure the reach of integrity. But it had raised Jon Sander to his full stature; or had Jon simply used it as the thing at hand, out of a deeper impulse? Religion seemed to stand aside and wait for better questions, as if it were enough for a man to know that he was made in the image and as a final sacrifice had better give up the deliberate search for God until he had learned to do his work better. To erase the common stain.

It was Michael who taught Ulen the value of questioning, but he had to find within himself the capacity for quiet in which to do it. To the mystic's cry: What Art Thou; What Am I? there came at first only a pulsation: That Art Thou. But the pulsation was still a question, for That is light, unformed and sourceless, and in time the great question divided so that he could ask alone: What Art Thou? When he could, it grew in light and power and moved him into growth too. As it did, the second question shrank: And I? For the answer to that was: "Nicodemus," and when he could accept it he found that he could accept the share of the common stain that came with it, not as a burden but as a law whose gradual resolution into custom and final cleansing into intuitive good living it was possible for him to help a little forward.

II

Aftermath of the Cases

WITH THAT I might rest my case, but there is still a breath to be drawn.

Ulen often felt a submerged curiosity about his litigants after they had left him, but rarely did he run across them again or hear of their subsequent doings. To set afoot an investigation of his own might be detected, and his curiosity was not worth the distress it might cause by refreshing old wounds that were often best forgotten after healing. He thought that it was nonsense to tell any litigant, particularly a convicted criminal, that the case should be a lesson to him. Most likely it was, without his having to say so, and his word for it wouldn't make it one if it wasn't. He believed that in the long run nature seals off wounds to pride or even to freedom in the way it seals off an abscess, and that a trial that does no more than inflict such a wound eventually leaves little trace or anything of lasting value. It was another demonstration that punishment inflicted from without is relatively useless, and that the counter-irritants set up against it by the human spirit are as malevolent or as wasteful as the original crime.

Ulen returned to his office from lunch one day a little late. Miss Dingle was sitting behind her typewriter a trifle more erect than usual, tapping the end of a pencil lightly against her lower teeth. Jim Tobey was in his chair looking at his feet. The room had an air of particular thoughtfulness and a kind of abashed expectancy. In another chair sat a nun, immobile as a column of obsidian. Her dark eyebrows matched her habit. Her lips were working silently and she moved her beads with a little flicking motion of her thumb. Having been led always to expect a second nun if he saw a first, he raised an inquiring eyebrow at Miss Dingle, who measured him thoughtfully in return. She was so astute in handling the variety of guests who sought him that to see her in an obvious quandary amused him. The other nun, he concluded, is within, and Miss Dingle can't quite understand how she managed to get there; but she did, and right under Miss Dingle's nose too. She nodded at him slightly and even more slightly shrugged her shoulders. For some reason she had given up. His eyebrow became ironically reproachful and he walked into his inner office.

It was not another nun that sat beside his table, but Perle. She arose when he entered and held out her hand to him with an effusiveness that he did not remember from his earlier experience with her. The small, finely cut face had stretched a little, as if a thin cloud had settled on it and remained, and her eyes had a flat and studied look. For some reason he felt distinctly on guard and took her hand perfunctorily, unable to suppress altogether the cold wave that beat outwards from him.

"Please forgive me for coming," she said and stopped in embarrassment.

He took a chair across the table from her and she resumed her seat, twisting into it warily as if expecting it to eject her without warning. He waited for her to go on, seeing no reason to make it easy for her.

"You were very kind to me here," she said, looking up at him near the end of her sentence with a little wrench of her head. 'We thought – I mean, I thought it would be good to come back for a few minutes and be sure of it."

"Oh?" said Ulen, lifting his eyebrows, "and why is that?"

Perle regarded the opposite wall for a moment and then nodded slightly towards the outer office.

"Well, perhaps you can see how it is," she replied, fastening her eyes upon him with an effort. "I've got a new idea about life. I'm converted."

Ulen's eyebrows went up again politely.

"Since when?" he inquired.

Perle seemed a trifle vague. "Oh, for quite a while," she answered. "I've had my ups and downs since I was here last."

"No doubt," Ulen murmured. "What happened to Joe?"

She seemed relieved to be on familiar ground and spoke more freely.

"He got a divorce," she said, "but I got him back again about a year later. Just as you suggested. We didn't get along so good for a while, but it's been better since – " Her voice trailed off into uncertainty.

"Since what?"

"Since I've been saved. Now I can save him too and it will be all right." She produced a brilliant smile.

Ulen was not as amused as he might have been by such a statement. The whole thing didn't make sense to him but he couldn't put his finger on anything. He wasn't too well acquainted with the customs of the Church, but there seemed to be something out of place, something unskilful and abrupt. He could find nothing to say and turned his head to look out of the window. Perle appeared to have come to the end of her resources and arose awkwardly.

"Well, thank you," she said. "Your secretary remembered me. That's how I got in. Well, good-bye."

She held out her hand stiffly and he arose to take it.

"Good-bye," he said, wishing that he could have found something to say that might have cleared things up a little. "I hope everything turns out all right."

"I do too," she said heartily, and went out. It seemed an odd thing to say at that point. He closed the door behind her and puzzled over it for a moment, but no answer suggested itself and he dismissed it from his mind.

This had occurred a few days before he began one of his three months' terms of criminal court. About two months later he was startled, during the arraignments, to hear the clerk call out the names of Perle and Joe Munger and a third name that meant nothing to him. They came forward, Perle's eyes bent appraisingly on Ulen, and pleaded guilty to a charge of extortion and blackmail. The third person was a middle-aged woman with violent red hair and highly painted cheeks. Since they were the last on the list to be arraigned, the clerk called for the witnesses, who turned out to be a sheepish-looking man and a detective, and swore them.

A few brief questions from the deputy District Attorney brought out the story. It appeared that the sheepish-looking man, who lived in a country district, had come to town on business. He was a man of fairly substantial means, a point on which the defendants had apparently made some research in advance. In fact, they seemed to have acquainted themselves with his entire background and with his exact plans for coming to the city. Perle even arranged to take the trip with him and struck up an acquaintance with him on the train. The acquaintance ripened so rapidly that at Perle's suggestion he took her to a small but convenient hotel and registered as man and wife. Since they had arrived in the early afternoon, Perle tactfully excused herself, in order not to interfere with his business, and rejoined him at dinner, after having conferred with her companions. He was so anxious to know her better that they retired to their room immediately after the meal and went to bed. It was not at all unnatural, at such an early hour, that the chambermaid should unlock their door with her passkey in order to tidy the room, and to be so shocked by what she saw that she went at once for a detective. Joe and the middle-aged woman, who had taken a room across the hall, played these parts with such conviction that the terrified victim ultimately produced ten thousand dollars to enable Joe, as the false detective, to buy off the police. This made such a dent in his finances that he had to explain it at home, and he did so in forlorn dismay to his brother-in-law, who had a vigorous personality and was a lawyer. The brother-in-law refused to let the matter drop: he hired a real detective and with his relative's reluctant help had the defendants apprehended while preparing to carry out their next case. They were able to provide cash bail out of the prosecutor's money.

Ulen was troubled while he listened to this recital. It was not an unfamiliar pattern but there seemed to be something missing. Trying to evaluate the situation for the purposes of sentence, he recalled Perle's visit to his office and the story of her conversion, but he found that he could neither accept nor dismiss its significance. He hadn't put much credence in it when he heard it, but faced with the necessity of sentencing her, he had to fit it in. It didn't fit and he had to suspend it in his mind until he could get the whole picture more clearly.

"Who is this person?" he asked the detective, pointing at the other woman.

"We don't know much about her," the detective answered, looking at her sideways, "except that she was on the stage once – in burlesque – and has been arrested a few times for minor offenses."

The prosecutor fidgeted, and when the detective had finished he raised his hand to speak.

"May I say something, Judge?" he asked. Ulen nodded. "She didn't have red hair when I saw her."

Ulen flung himself back in his chair as the light burst upon him. A wave of anger surged over him and before he could control it he said: "I don't think she had either, when she came to my office dressed up as a nun." He looked at her coldly and added: "You forgot your eyebrows."

He restrained himself and gazed down at them severely.

So. Did they think he was such a fool? Well, he nearly had been: he might have let that story of Perle's influence him, even a little. He snorted to himself grimly, and suddenly remembered Councill's asking him how he re-imagined Perle's case after he had told it at Artema's lunch that day. He hadn't been able to, and they had taken advantage of his efforts by thinking him a sentimental fool. He still felt angry and uncomfortable. He looked wrathfully at the three figures sagging before him at the bar of the court, the starch out of them. Perle ventured only one look at him but it sank again at once. Her face had an unhealthy pallor and for a fleeting instant the tragedy of a human being on the skids filled his mind: but maybe she was trying that on too, and he hardened. Once he had thought that she had integrity and he couldn't help wondering what had happened to bring her and Joe to this pass. But it wouldn't help to know now. The situation had moved beyond the point where finding out would mean anything. He said nothing for a minute or two and then leaned forward.

"I won't sentence you now," he said shortly. "I'm angry and it wouldn't do. I'll remand you to jail over night and sentence you in the morning."

The case cost him no sleep, and after thinking about it for a little while after supper he shrugged his shoulders and went to bed. It was one of the many cases that gave him nothing to hold to or work with. At least he hadn't sentenced them while he was angry: anger gave the victims of it a sense of power. He had to jolt them but he'd do it coolly. That might have an effect on them. It was the most he could do.

"You know perfectly well what I must do to you," he told

them the next morning. "The only constructive thing I can think of is to keep you apart from each other."

He sent them to separate prisons for five years.

Once or twice when Ulen went to the County Prison he inquired about Bring, and the news disturbed him a little. Had the boy merely made a nuisance of himself it would have been different, but the warden, when Ulen asked him about it, shook his head glumly. Bring, it seemed, had attached himself to a small but implacable group of prisoners, headed by a confirmed criminal, who effectually ruled the institution. They did not rob their fellows; they simply levied tribute for protection and slugged those from whom it was not forthcoming. One well-executed plan for escape had been thwarted at the last minute, and Bring had played a leading part in it.

Ulen asked to see the boy and looked idly around him while he waited. There being little work for the prisoners, they were set to keeping the place clean, and the ancient building had the faint odor of a very old butterchurn; it was so clean it was almost fetid. The walls were whitewashed until they resembled a corridor through a snowbank, and the gray stone floors were dark from the damp of recent scrubbing. In every direction there were gleaming steel gates which were unlocked and locked again for everyone passing through. It was a vise of gray and white, as if to punish even a man's eyes by denying them color. Gray for steel; and white, the color used to cover things with.

Bring swung around the corner and faced him. He had been brought from a solitary cell, where he was resting on bread and water for a few days after having slugged another prisoner. Ulen could get nothing from him, and after looking at him closely did not try, for the boy's defenses were up and Ulen knew that he would give out only what he thought was expected of him. The warden could be of greater help, and Ulen let the boy go after a few words that evoked no response but a look. Knowing Bring's history, the warden was puzzled but did not think of asking for Ulen's opinion; he was caught in the cage of which he was in charge, mentally less free than those whom he kept under lock and key. Ulen left, rubbing his chin thoughtfully. Rather more than he had bargained for, but somehow he felt that Bring was on the right track, only too much so, and secretively. Too violently in reverse, wanting to be dominated by the older criminal and seeking freedom covertly.

Ulen could not parole him on such a prison record, and Bring served his full two years. After leaving prison he disappeared. Ulen looked up the police records once or twice within the next year or two, but there was no word of him. Maybe he had left town. Then one day he saw in the paper that Bring had been wounded in a gun duel with three armed men, two of whom were later apprehended. The story went on to say that Bring was carrying the payroll of a small concern for which he was working when he was set upon, and that he had fatally wounded one of his assailants. The man later died in the prison hospital. Ulen frowned and called up the warden. Bring's victim was the leader of the gang to which he had attached himself in prison. "Mr. Bring," the story concluded, "has a wife and a son, aged six months."

Due to his accident, Ulen never heard the Alberson case. It was handled by another judge, who took an instant dislike to Aletha and Henry, and not only voided their deed but threw them out of Professor Alberson's home and left Alice there, with the Professor as her guardian. He had tactfully asked Parkinson to transfer the earlier proceedings to him, in order to dispose of the entire controversy at one time, and Parkinson had been glad to be rid of it. Probably no better solution could have been found, for even the law could not supply confidence when reason for having none became apparent, but it left Professor Alberson in the familiar position of having a victory and not knowing what to do with it. Both Alice and the house needed looking after, and he had no idea of how to go about it. In this way the evil of Aletha and Henry lived after them, set in motion, as evil often is, by the Professor's poor judgment in trusting them in the first place. The judge did not sign his decree until the lawyer assured him that the old people would be cared for. In fact, he made it a condition of his decree, and it is likely that Professor Alberson ended his days in front of his fire, puzzling over the expense but feeling secretly a little pleased with himself.

It was considerably later, on the afternoon before Julia's death, when he had thrown aside the Alberson case and decided to look in at the museum, that he met Sara. The old building with its immense ceilings always quieted him, as it did everyone that came there, for people walked about with the slower pace of the vanished centuries whose best essence was on display. It took time to appreciate the best, he thought, since the average tread of life is at a lower level and mountain air is a little unfamiliar. He headed for Geology. There was a group of women talking together when he crossed the vestibule, and he heard his name called. He turned to see Mrs. Councill holding out her hand to him and he stopped with pleasure to speak to her.

"May I introduce my friend Mrs. Bardelman?" she said, after amenities.

Ulen looked up in surprise. Sara did not hesitate. He saw her face slicing towards him, and before he knew it she had put her hands on his shoulders with a tinkling rattle of bracelets and kissed him firmly on the cheek.

"You don't mind, do you?" she said, backing off a step and looking at him eagerly. "There were no thanks, ever. You know that and so do I."

Of course he didn't mind, he said; he wouldn't have had her fail in spontaneity for anything – it wouldn't have been like her if she had.

It was strange, meeting her like that. They had never spoken to each other personally, and with the case between them, it was as if they were standing together beside a dark well and tossing lighted bits of themselves into it. Once she had been at the bottom of it and he at the top, and the burden was on her to take her place beside him now. He knew that and helped her. She managed it with startling rapidity and turned to Mrs. Councill to explain.

"I want to talk to him," she concluded, "and I'm going to take him off into a corner where I can. Have you a little time?" Her gray eyes had decided that he had, and he was happy to be led away.

He looked at her while they walked along. Her hair was

drawn tightly around her head, the part leading straight through the middle to a knot at the top of her neck. Ulen had the impression that the fire in her, which had once been scattered through her, had been compressed into her eyes, leaving the rest of her thinner and somehow more firmly tied together. Although she could be only twenty-two or so, there was a small curved line at each corner of her mouth, as if done by one clear cut of a chisel. The brushfire of her eyes that he remembered was now concentrated in a flame so penetrating that she had the air of saying only a part of what she took in, and he saw that she was one of those people who are ceaselessly at work. He resigned himself to her involuntary attack and sat down with her in a corner of the Mosaics Room, which few people ever visited. She drew a long breath and modelled him swiftly; this done, she let go and waited for him. He noticed it and ventured a remark.

"Now that you have made a statue of me," he observed, "we can talk. Didn't you ever try it before?"

"Yes, I did try it," she replied, "but nothing came out—just a suggestion of a body with a robe around it, against a rough wall of marble, but the head never did come through. It couldn't. An artist can't work unless he has the upper hand, and needless to say, I didn't have it. An artist can't work in fear either, and I was frightened of that head of yours and of what it would do to me."

He saw that her eyes could die down a little. She was almost pensive, and the young lines around her mouth had shallowed.

"This head of mine," he said, "is supposed to do only what is generally sensible. Too bad that what's generally sensible has to sneak about and hide in someone else's skull, causing distress until it gathers itself so that he can lay hands on it." He paused and twisted himself around to look at her squarely. "Mrs. Bardelman – did I hear correctly?"

She laughed and fumbled at the clasp of her necklace below the knot of her hair, her head bent.

"You heard correctly, and will hear more." She drew off the necklace and opened a locket that hung from it. "I introduce Miss June Bardelman," she went on, "aged ten months."

Ulen took the locket and looked at it. "Hardly any age at all," he remarked. "But the fact is ageless, and it is always, particularly sometimes, very wonderful indeed. That's all I can say."

She fastened on the necklace again and there was an awkward pause.

"Why are you here, just today?" she asked.

"Oh, I drop in now and then to look at the geology exhibit," he replied. "After the bitter little splinters of time that I have to stick into people, it's comforting to look at the record of years by the hundreds of millions. It's a cooling kind of escape, I imagine. Why are you here?"

"I have something on show," she said, pointing with her eyes. "In there. Oh no, not now, please." She laid a hand quickly on his arm when he started to get up. "I want you to see it later, by yourself. You have a question about me in your mind and you'll get the best answer that way."

"All right," he said. "You know better about that. Certainly I have a question and I'll ask part of it. What are you after, in your work?"

She let her eyes roam about for a moment, and he could see that she was only looking for words.

"What's generally true but unobserved," she said after a moment. "Just as you are after what's generally sensible and should be known at once. But I came to a curious discovery. I can't do it well enough. The thing in there isn't general, it's straight me. That won't give anything away, for you'll see it quickly enough. You do understand, don't you?"

"Only too well," he answered, "and no answer could be more reassuring. But there's another part of the question. How's Jon?"

"Jon's in California," she said, a shade too quickly, "taking a pre-medical course." She fell silent at once.

Ulen looked at her steadily. "What is it, Sara?" he asked without emphasis.

She glanced up at him.

"I don't quite know," she said with candor. "We're in a kind of recess, Jon and I, without either of us wanting to be. Something in us hit and bounced, and there's a vacuum we can't get back across. You said something during the—the case, that if I could forgive myself he would say nothing. Well, I did and he didn't, and yet here we are. I don't understand it; I thought it had made us closer than we ever were."

"You may have to wait," Ulen observed.

"Why?"

"Too much, too soon." He paused, thinking how to get at it gently. No use in that; she was too direct.

"What were your relations with Jon based on, way down and in the beginning?" he asked. "Did you get him fairly?"

She shook her head a little savagely and knotted her chin.

"No. That's the answer and I know it," she said. "What's the price?"

"An illusion, as usual," he said evenly. "You'll always have to be grown-ups together. The older thing is gone, I'm afraid. I hope you're ready to accept it."

She got up like a rising wind and held out her hand to him.

"Not quite," she said, and the lines around her mouth deepened again. "I must get back to my friends. They're a kind of committee for me, and they've made this possible. Thanks; you've been good for me. Will you look in and see it?"

There was a flash from the gray eyes. He smiled and watched her hurry away. He went to Geology and strolled about until the committee had dispersed, and then made his way to the room in which Sara's statue was showing. He found it readily and sat down in a chair against the wall to look at it. The room was quiet, and the fading daylight shone on the little figure before him. It was a bronze statue about two feet high of a young girl on one knee. She may have been an angel, for she had one great soaring wing, but the face, still earthbound, was turned upward with a slight smile of question. The body was tense, and with one hand she was lifting the other wing, which lay on the ground before her. After he had read the question and the tension in her young body he saw that the hand that was lifting the wing had clutched it until the feathers were crushed and broken between her fingers.

He gazed at the statue attentively for some time, but when Sara, whose curiosity was still a little too much for her, peeked around the corner, his head had fallen forward on his chest and he was sleeping.

A NOTE ON THE TYPE

The text of this book is set in Caledonia, a Linotype face which belongs to the family of printing types called "modern face" by printers — a term used to mark the change in style of type-letters that occurred about 1800. Caledonia borders on the general design of Scotch Modern, but is more freely drawn than that letter.

The book was composed, printed, and bound by The Plimpton Press, Norwood, Massachusetts. The typography and binding are based on original designs by W. A. Dwiggins.